HOW TO RUN A MARATHON

The Complete Guide for First-Time and Amateur Marathoners

Heather Mull-Stricek

Copyright © Heather Mull-Stricek, 2000

All Rights Reserved. No part of this publication may be reproduced, stored in a retrieval system, or transmitted in any form or by any means – electronic, mechanical, photocopying, recording, or otherwise – without prior written permission from the publisher.

Published by Sigma Leisure – an imprint of
Sigma Press, 1 South Oak Lane, Wilmslow, Cheshire SK9 6AR, England.

British Library Cataloguing in Publication Data
A CIP record for this book is available from the British Library.

ISBN: 1-85058-746-9

Typesetting and Design by: Sigma Press, Wilmslow, Cheshire.

Printed by: MFP Design & Print

Cover Design: The Agency, Macclesfield.

Photographs: Mart Bosman

Just an idea ...

The petite Kenyan woman raced towards us at an amazing pace. We watched in awe as Tegla Loroupe ran past to win the marathon in a slick 2 hours, 22 minutes and 7 seconds. The best man and overall winner – Portuguese Domingos Castro – had run past earlier to finish in 2:07.51. 'I wouldn't mind having a go at this next year,' I casually remarked to Mart. However offhand the remark, a seed had been planted in my mind – and there wasn't really any turning back from there.

Women's marathon world record holder, Tegla Loroupe, about to finish in the 1999 Rotterdam marathon.

This scene unfolded at the 1997 Dutch Rotterdam marathon, where Tegla had narrowly missed bettering the 1985 world record time of 2:21.06 set in London by Norwegian runner Ingrid Kristiansen. Rotterdam was my first glimpse of a world-class marathon, and being able to see superbly trained athletes passing by was a real pleasure. Maybe the fact that they made the running look so easy played some part in my determining to be in the 1998 marathon, but I wasn't the only one thinking that way. Tegla also vowed to be there again for another shot at the longstanding world record she wanted to claim.

Originally from a country town in Victoria, Australia, I moved to Holland in 1996. And now I had the exciting opportunity to take part in a world-renowned marathon. It was a chance I seized – but successfully? You bet! I finished my first marathon a little wiser, a lot wearier, and ecstatic with my new achievement. How about Tegla? She also ran again and did claim a new world record in a time of 2:20.47, with a nice bonus cash prize for her efforts. (She would go on to break the record again two years later in Berlin, during her 13th marathon, with a time of 2:20.43). But the beauty of the event is that even though there were so many runners between her and I, we could both experience the thrill of crossing the finish line. We succeeded in achieving different personal goals, which before the marathon started had simply been question marks.

So why write this book? When I wanted to begin marathon training I had difficulty finding a book that would tell me all I wanted to know as a first-timer. I couldn't find some of the really basic information I needed. Consequently some of the content of this book was learnt through trial and error! Due to the short time between my achievement and the writing of this book, I can recall the joys and frustrations I experienced leading up to, during and even after the marathon. I wanted to share my experiences with other aspiring marathoners, to help make a marathon achievable and as pleasurable as possible for you.

The training programme contained within this book can guide you towards such an experience in **four months.** This book takes a lot of the guesswork out of the process, and gives an insight into how to avoid mistakes that I made in the weeks before walking up to the start line.

So now all that stands between you and a marathon finish line is the following collection of pages (and a bit of preparation work on your part of course!). Happy reading and running!

Inline skating on a bike path in Holland. A good form of aerobic exercise and one I was able to do when recovering from a knee injury. (In Chapter 5).

Heather Mull-Stricek

Acknowledgements

This book is dedicated to my family, and every person who has ever supported me in my past sporting endeavours.

I would like to thank several friends for their help in the making of this book:

Mart Bosman – for taking most of the photographs, and for his ongoing encouragement, support and belief that this book would be successful.

Noel Whittall – for giving me my first insights into the world of writing, and for patiently answering my "How do I?" questions.

Ingrid Vasilakis (medical specialist) – for all her proof-reading and help with the medical bits (and to her husband – Jorgos – for entertaining us with his snail stories!).

Ebred Reynen – for putting the idea of running the Rotterdam marathon into my head, and for collecting newspaper clippings for me.

Boo (Katrina Glass) and Jon Clayton – for their initial encouraging comments.

Sandra and Terry Stubbs – for their advice and great barbecues!

Those **Rhoon inhabitants** who greeted and encouraged me as I trained.

Training programme plan adapted from *Marathon Training* by J. Henderson, 1997. (Champaign, IL: Human Kinetics), 13.

Sample diary page adapted from *Marathon Training* by J. Henderson, 1997. (Champaign, IL: Human Kinetics), 19.

Contents

Chapter One
Which Marathon?   *1*
   Who can run a marathon?   3
   Which one?   4

Chapter Two
The Training Programme   *9*
   My training background in brief   9
   Choosing a training programme   10
   An effective programme   11
   The programme's content   12
   Description of training terms used   12
   Rest Days   14
   Training Programme Plan   14
   Rationale behind the training format   17
   Training Records   18

Chapter Three
Training Logistics   *24*
   Where and when to train   24
   Bad weather   25
   Marathon rehearsals   25
   Running technique   30
   Stress monitoring   31
   Training Tips   34

Chapter Four
Clothing   *36*
   Clothes for daily training   36
   What will I wear during the marathon?   37
   Accessories   38
   Running Shoes   38
   Tips to Get the Right Shoes   41

Chapter Five
Complications Along the Way   *43*
   Away from home   43
   Getting a stitch   44
   Injuries   45
     Knee lock   45
     Torn muscle   46
     Inflamed tendons and blisters 48

More knee trouble   49
Leg muscle tenderness   50
Frame of mind   52

Chapter Six
What to Eat   **54**
Carbohydrates (CHO)   54
Fats   55
Protein   58
Vitamins and minerals   59
Fibre   60
Water   61
Eating habits   62
Before and after training   64
Breakfast   65
Lunch   66
Snacks   68
Dinner   68
Sweet-tooth Saturday   70
Preparing for the marathon   71
    The day before   71
    Marathon day   71
    During the marathon   72
    After the marathon   72

Chapter Seven
Especially for Women   **74**
Marathons for women   74
Menstruation and the athlete   75
Pre-menstrual syndrome (PMS)   75
Amenorrhoea (lack or loss of periods) and Osteoporosis   78
Anaemia   79
Pregnancy and training   80
Menopause   81
Bras   82
Make-up   83
Eating disorders   84
    Normal BMI Ranges   87
De-stressing   87

Chapter Eight
Common Running Injuries   **90**
General definitions and R.I.C.E   90
Foot and ankle injuries   92
    Plantar fasciitis   92

Sprained ankle 93
Achilles tendinitis 94
Shin splints 95
Knee pain 96
Muscle strains 98
Cramp 99
Sciatica and back pain 100
Knowing when to stop 101

Chapter Nine
The Final Weeks 103
Tapering training 103
Staying healthy 103
Race information 104
Other preparations 106

Chapter Ten
The Big Day! 109
Final preparations 109
The night before 110
Marathon morning 111
At the start 112
Run tactics 112
Straight afterwards 114

Chapter Eleven
What to Expect Afterwards 116
Happy memories 116
Recovering 117

Chapter Twelve
Stretching Exercises 120

Chapter 13
Fax to Family – 20/4/98 125

Chapter 14
Afterword 132

Chapter 15
Suggested Reading 133

Your Marathon Training Diary 133

Chapter One

Which Marathon?

"Only those who dare to fail greatly can ever achieve greatly." – Robert Kennedy

Making the decision to run a marathon can be the result of a number of reasons. Maybe some of your reasons are similar to the ones I had – like the desire to really test my physical and mental abilities. Running a marathon is certainly one good way to do that. The conventional marathon is 42.195 kilometres in length, but there are also ultra-marathons that are up to 100km and longer. For the purposes of this book I will be referring to the conventional distance.

The marathon race came into existence to commemorate the legendary feat of a Greek soldier named Pheidippides. It is said that in 490BC he ran approximately 36km from the battlefield of Marathon in Athens with news of the Athenian victory over the Persians. Upon shouting, 'Rejoice! We conquer!' he then died

The start of the Rotterdam Marathon – note the varieties of attire

of exhaustion! The first marathon was held at the 1896 Olympic Games in Athens, and the distance was standardised to 42.195km in 1924.

Completing a marathon is not an easy achievement; if it were then any untrained person could do one. Your abilities are also tested during the training phase in the months before the event. I always like the feeling of having achieved, but with the marathon there is that underlying uncertainty of whether you will actually complete the whole 42.195km. Part of the thrill is in knowing that even after months of preparation you will only know you have completely succeeded when you cross the finishing line.

The Rotterdam marathon gave me the opportunity to be part of a world-renowned event. To know that I was running in the same footsteps as some of the world's best athletes was a special feeling. Just making it to your first marathon day increases your sense of self-esteem and pride, and these feelings are even more amplified when you actually cross the finishing line. Then there is the "afterglow" feeling – something that stays with you for a long time and which causes you to smile whenever anything reminds you of your success.

I only ever really wanted to run one marathon, just to see if I could. In earlier years I had run several half-marathons and I always wondered then if I would ever do a full one. My personal motto has always been 'Just do it' – long before Nike made it famous with their commercials. If there is something you really want to do, then make it a goal and 'Just do it!' Telling other people of your goal is also a good idea, as it makes you more committed to seeing it through to the end (words carry their own energy!). In my case the marathon also marked two years to the date that I had arrived in Holland from Australia, so I thought it would be a fitting way to celebrate the anniversary if I could achieve a long-held ambition on that day. The first person I let know about this goal was my boyfriend, Mart. He had also been a keen runner in the past but had stopped because of knee problems. Nevertheless, he supported me in every way that he could in the lead-up to and during the marathon. It's nice to have someone to really encourage you through the tougher training days.

Who can run a marathon?

Basically anyone with a strong enough desire to complete one. Once you have set the goal to run a certain marathon, then you need to dedicate some time to training adequately for it. Due to the long distance, it is a good idea if before you begin serious training you are familiar with the feeling of jogging for at least one hour without stopping and have also in the past taken part in some 5 to 10km races. Deciding to run 42.195km on an inadequate preparation is a sure way to cause yourself physical and mental distress. I recall a friend recounting how her brother-in-law had done a marathon with only a few training runs of 5km or so. He did finally finish but suffered major pain for days afterwards due to knees and legs that resembled inflated cushions!

Of course there are differences in the training programmes of the fastest competitors compared with those of the casual runner, but as long as you choose and follow through with the right programme for you then you should be able to experience the marathon with pleasure rather than in agony. Don't feel that you have to be a remarkably talented athlete to begin a training programme, as the majority of participants nowadays are members of the general population as opposed to being elite athletes. Maybe you think you are too short, tall, fat, weak or old to take part, but rest assured that marathoners come in all shapes, sizes and ages. Never judge someone's ability to run a marathon by looks alone. I consider myself to be quite fit and in pretty good shape, but to my surprise there were plenty of larger women (with an abundance of visible cellulite) who ran just as easily and faster than I did. Stamina is what plays the major role in a marathon, not how svelte you are! On the other hand, if the world record is what you're aiming for then weighing in at around 42kg like Tegla certainly means a lighter load to carry for 42.195km!

The marathon is also an event that people with a variety of handicaps have succeeded at. Some marathons have categories for wheelchair competitors. In the past these have included marathons in cities such as Berlin, Prague and Boston, to name a few. At Rotterdam '98 there was a blind participant who successfully completed the distance with the help of his guide dog. A short time after in an American marathon there was the re-

markable story of a woman with multiple sclerosis who completed the distance in 38 hours, with an arm support in each
hand. Such inspirational stories abound in the marathon world.

Which one?

If you are attempting your first marathon then it is worthwhile
doing some research into which one you want to do, to give
yourself as much chance of finishing as possible. Don't decide to
do one in a month's time. Make sure that you have at least a minimum of three to four months of training time between now and
race day. This ensures time for an adequate preparation and also
gives you some breathing space if you have to recover from a
training injury along the way.

Consider the **time of year** and the **climate** in the area of the
marathon you choose. Marathons are run in most months of the
year but you may have a preference about running in warmer or
cooler weather. Of course there is no guarantee that the weather
on the day will be just how you want it – that's one factor that
you don't have a final say in! To my way of thinking the weather
in Rotterdam '98 was pretty perfect. The day started off cool and
overcast and the temperature eventually reached about 13 degrees Celsius. This was great for running in as there wasn't a
problem of overheating (unless you were wearing too many
clothes). The temperature did get cooler a few hours into the
run, but overall it was a good day weather-wise.

The **ideal weather conditions** for fast marathon times include an air temperature of around 12-14 degrees Celsius, a
slightly overcast sky with humidity about 80%, and little or no
wind. Since 1981, the temperatures in the Rotterdam marathon
have ranged between a chilly 6.4 degrees in 1986 up to 21.3 degrees the very next year! It pays to be prepared for all conditions.
In 1999 the 10-degree day turned out to be a bit colder than in
1998. Neither of the Kenyan winners was able to break the
world record. The winning male was Japhet Kosgei in 2:07.09,
and Tegla Loroupe was the first female again in 2:22.50. The
cooler conditions definitely adversely affected their world record attempts.

The **terrain** a marathon covers is worth considering. Usually
marathons take place on bitumen roadways, and depending on

where it is organised the amount of uphill can vary markedly. The Rotterdam marathon course is great for first timers in that there are basically no uphill sections at all. The uphill rise over the entire course is only about 20 metres. This is one reason why such fast times can be run there. When I ran my half marathons years ago, they were all over a reasonably hilly course. There was also a full marathon attached to the event, and in hindsight I can really appreciate how much harder it must have been for runners doing their marathons through that hilly Australian course. I'm glad that I waited until coming to Holland before attempting my first one!

Look at the **history** of the event you choose. The likelihood is that the longer this particular marathon has been occurring, the better the overall organisation will be. The 1998 Rotterdam marathon was the city's eighteenth, and with the participants numbering in excess of 10,000 effective organisation was necessary. From a participant's point of view everything seemed to go very smoothly for the organisers, from the two days prior when competitors picked up their numbers right through to the end of the run. When the Rotterdam marathon was first held back in 1981, there were only 220 runners. These days around 1500 volunteers are needed to cope with all the runners' requirements on the day.

The **number** of participants and spectators might also be important. The idea of running with 10,000 or more other people might not actually appeal to you, but for me that provided one of the most interesting sensations, as I train almost all the time on my own. For the first few kilometres everyone was busy weaving and dodging through the sea of bodies until they could settle into their own rhythm. Also amazing was being cheered on by some 800,000 spectators – at times their cries of 'keep going' made me quite emotional. The atmosphere they created for the duration of the marathon was really something very special to experience.

Does your chosen marathon have a **time limit**? Many of the better-known ones set a time limit for the runners of between 4.5 and 6 hours from start to finish. Rotterdam's course began in the city then made loops to the south and north before finishing back at the starting place. In order to do this the streets were closed for a good part of the day. There was a limit of 5 hours placed on the marathon runners and then the streets were opened to traffic again. The slowest runner actually took 5 hours 12minutes. So make sure you know of any such restrictions beforehand, rather than being surprised on the day.

You may decide to **travel** to another country to take part in a famous marathon for your first time. In that event you will have to take into consideration the ease and cost of getting there. Ideally you should arrive a few days before the event to settle in, rather than just the night before, but this will be dependent on any time restraints you have with a job or family responsibilities. Travelling costs to the venue may also need to be budgeted for in advance if an airfare or many petrol stops are required. If you can convince a friend to run the same marathon then not only will you have a training partner but someone to share the travel expenses as well if getting there involves a long drive!

Regardless of the marathon you choose, **entering** it is obviously a necessary part of the process. Make sure that you are aware of the entry requirements months in advance of the run. Some marathons accept only a set number of competitors, the entry form usually has to be received well in advance and the entry fee can increase as the deadline gets closer. By getting entry details early you will not be surprised by particular race limitations imposed by specific events. You will also enhance your chances of being able to run the marathon of your choice.

I really had no idea of how to go about entering the Rotterdam marathon until a friend gave me an organising contact number. I rang six weeks before the event (having just returned from a summer vacation in Australia), hoping I was not too late to enter. Luckily I wasn't and they mailed me an entry form, but the entry fee of 70 gulden was already higher than if I had entered earlier. I waited anxiously for four weeks until I saw the entry fee amount deducted from my bank account – what a relief, and definitely no turning back then – I was in! Shortly afterwards there followed an information package about the race details and when and where I was to pick up my competitor number.

Only later in my race number "goodies" bag did I find an informative magazine called *Distance Running* which contained results reports from a number of recent marathons as well as advertisements for marathons and entry forms from all over the world. There were also pages of "race contact details" outlining the countries and names of all the better-known half, full and ultra marathons and who to contact for further information and entry forms. This magazine is produced in January and July each year and is an official publication of the Association of International Marathons and Road Races and the International Amateur Athletic Federation. It is distributed at races worldwide but you can also subscribe personally by contacting:

Distance Running, 14 Elliot Place, Finnieston, Glasgow, G3 8EP, Scotland, United Kingdom.
Telephone +44 (0) 141 221 9136, fax +44 (0) 141 226 5575, e-mail drunmag@aol.com

Another method of finding out about marathons in your own area is to contact local running or other sports clubs who can guide you in the right direction. The bottom line is, find out all the details and enter early.

When reflecting on my whole marathon experience I can identify some different stages, and you may recognise similar ones in your quest for success too. They are as follows:

- Making the decision to do it and sending in the entry form.

- Choosing a good training programme.

- Putting in the hard work.

- Doubting my sanity during the long training sessions – would I be able to finish the whole 42.195km?

- Confirmation of my entry.

- Tapering my training closer to the event.

- The final week and worrying about being struck down by illness.

- Pre-marathon nerves.

- Today is the day, and "Doing it".

- The elation and "electric" post-run feelings.

- The period of recovery and reflecting on 'Yes, I did actually do it!'

Chapter One Summary

⇨ Set a goal to complete a marathon sometime within the next year.

⇨ Choose a marathon you would like to do, taking factors like location, time of year, climate, terrain and run time limit into consideration.

⇨ Find out the entry details and enter early.

⇨ Ensure that you have enough training time before the marathon (3 or 4 months or longer).

⇨ Follow a training programme that is suitable for your ability level (see Chapter 2).

Chapter Two
The Training Programme

"To follow your pathway to success, YOU need to put in the kilometres."

My training background in brief

Showing an interest in reading this book would suggest that you have probably been involved in running (or are interested in it) and maybe other sports as well in your past. Sport has always played a major role in my life. As a teenager I was a keen participant in the local tennis and swimming clubs and Nordic skiing. I loved competitive running at high school, from 100m to 3000m distances. At sixteen, I ran a local half marathon comfortably in a time of 1:52.00. Between then and 1991 I ran the same race five times more, with varying degrees of success as dictated by my current fitness level and weight (which annoyingly fluctuated by several kilos at times!). My best time was a 1:37.52. Each time I wondered if I would ever be running the longer 42.195km event.

At university I studied to become a Physical Education/Science secondary school teacher, and became involved in triathlons, biathlons (a combination of Nordic Skiing and shooting) and also trained seriously for one year as a bodybuilder. I competed in Nordic ski races from the ages of 12 to 26, travelling to Europe twice in Australian teams. I also took up hang-gliding at the end of 1988, which I still enjoy immensely. My last year of serious training for skiing was in 1991, and after that I just did some regular cycling and jogging to keep in shape.

In April 1996 I shifted to the village of Rhoon, in Holland, and my training temporarily fell by the wayside. We do much of our summer hang-gliding in France, and by August I had gained several kilograms from a summer of too many French pastries and bread. On returning to Holland I decided to recommence training to get back into shape. I began running again, usually five times per week for 30 to 35 minutes. We also went to a gym for strength workouts twice a week. When the weather turned too wintry to be outside, I would do an aerobics workout – I definitely prefer not to train in bad weather conditions!

When I decided seriously to run the 1998 Rotterdam Marathon (held in April), it was already January 1998. Up until then I had just been doing my usual training runs and it was nearly seven years since my last long (half marathon) foot race. In Australia visiting my family, I set about looking for a book that would tell me how to prepare for a marathon. With some determined searching, I eventually found one that offered me success in 100 days, and I was happy that it would fit right into my time schedule. I chose and followed the programme I considered most suitable for me as accurately as I could. It did lead to success, but there was a lot to be learnt over those three preparation months.

Choosing a training programme

Assuming that you are a novice to marathons (or relatively so) then the programme in this book is aimed specifically at your level of training. It will guide you towards a solid marathon preparation, whether you want to just comfortably make the distance or if you also have a set time in mind. You also need to decide whether you will try to run the entire distance or use a combination of running with some walking intervals. If you're not sure, then once you're into the longer training runs you will have more of an idea of how you will cope with a marathon distance. Whatever you have in mind, it must be realistic for your level of ability. My aims for the marathon were to finish and, if everything was going to plan, **aim** for around the 4-hour mark.

So time wasn't initially important to me, but if all was going well then it would be an added bonus to finish in the vicinity of four hours. I wasn't too sure what time to aim for – and maybe a time is of no importance for your marathon – but I figured that I could run a half marathon comfortably in two hours (because I used to be able to!), so should be able to complete 42-km in four hours. I also wanted to complete the entire distance by running as much of it as possible, but decided that if I had to walk to finish then that would be okay too.

This programme would also be suitable if you are aiming for a time faster than four hours, but if you want information on how to **race** the distance for really fast times, then you need an advanced programme that utilises more speed and accurately paced sessions.

An effective programme

Ideally a good training programme should have a degree of **flexibility** so that you are able to complete your training sessions without jeopardising the rest of the daily schedule. A programme that is too rigid in terms of when and how you must train can have an adverse effect on family, work and other commitments. The programme offered here provides flexibility in that you are given the recommended workout times and/or distances, then it is up to you how these are slotted into each week. That way you can work around other commitments, juggle sessions because of a missed workout and even make alterations on the day if necessary.

An effective training programme makes use of a **variety** of training sessions. Earlier advice for marathoners was simply to run very long distances each week, which for some athletes translated into weekly distance totals of 200km or more. More popular now are training programmes which utilise short runs, fast runs, semi-long runs and rest days in combination with some longer runs to make for a more enjoyable but still effective preparation. A varied training programme appealed to me also because apart from not wanting to get bored by running only long distances every day, I didn't want to have to devote huge periods of time to training.

Training programmes for many sports have similar concepts to make them effective. One of these concepts is that of **periodisation.** This refers to dividing the training time (a year, the months or weeks) into periods of training sessions of differing intensity. There can be easy, medium or hard weeks within a month and similarly for the months in the year. For this programme it means scheduling easy, medium and harder training sessions within each week. The aim is to gradually increase the long run distances so that by marathon day you will be able to cope with the 42.195km distance, without having suffered injuries or **over-training** in the preparation period. Over-training is a condition whereby too much high distance/time training leads to severe body fatigue and a deterioration in performance. One guideline used when making changes in a training programme is to increase or change factors such as pace and distance by no more than 10% per week. This minimises the risk of overuse injuries.

The programme's content

This training programme consists of four differently named training sessions based on their level of **intensity.** Rest days are also included within the training week. It is a modification of the programme I followed, as outlined in the book *Marathon Training – The Proven 100 Day Programme for Success.* The author is Joe Henderson and the book was published in 1997 by Human Kinetics, USA. His book offers programmes for all levels of marathon runner and is a good source of information from someone who has been involved in the marathon scene for many years.

One of the main modifications in my programme aims to encourage runners used to regular 30 to 45-minute runs (as I was) rather than 1 hour plus-runs. Training in this programme begins three weeks earlier so that the length of the Medium Distance (MD) and Long Slow Distance (LSD) runs (see descriptions below) can be increased more gradually to begin with. If you are already comfortable with regular 1 to 1.5-hour runs, then you could probably begin this programme at week 4, but don't be tempted to 'shortcut' unless you are absolutely sure.

Description of training terms used

The different training sessions used are as follows:

Basic – this refers to the runs that make up the bulk of your training. They range between 30 and 60 minutes and are run at a comfortable pace (able to have a conversation with a companion whilst running). So 3 – 4 x 30 – 45 mins as shown in the programme for Week 1 would mean that you plan three or four runs of between 30 and 45 minutes each into that week.

SFD (short fast distance)/Race – these sessions consist of runs that put some speed into the workout. They are grouped together because it is up to you which sort you do.

Race – means that you run the distance as if you were in a race, so entails pushing yourself pretty hard the whole way. You can do this in a proper race at an event, or you can race on your own if you are used to pushing yourself as hard as you would in a race. At this pace you wouldn't really be able to have a decent conversation with anyone whilst running. The session time will last anywhere from 20 to 30 minutes.

SFD runs are also faster than basic runs, but not as fast as race pace. Done at a medium to hard intensity you need to consciously keep pushing yourself, so prolonged conversation with someone is not possible. These last from about 20 to 40 minutes. While trying to keep as close to my training schedule as possible, I found that these runs made an excellent substitute now and then when I really didn't feel like going out for a longer basic run. You don't have to be out running for as long, but because of the extra effort you still feel like the workout has been a good one!

MD (medium distance) – these are simply shorter versions of the LSD runs. Run at the same pace or slightly faster, they range from around 1 to 1.5 hours. These should be done without the walk intervals suggested in the LSD runs.

LSD (long, slow distance – not related to drugs in any way!) – these runs are vital to preparation as you use them to mimic what you will be doing during the marathon. The pace is slow and easy so that you can easily converse with a partner. As you become more familiar with the longer distances, the pace should go from slightly slower than your intended marathon pace to the pace you intend trying to run the marathon at. The times will range from around 1.5 hours to 3 hours or more. A good way to get used to these longer runs without too much physical discomfort is to incorporate some walk intervals into them. For runs of 1.5 hours or longer, walk for 2 to 5 minutes after each 25 minutes of running. Include these intervals in the total run time. They will help the body adapt more comfortably to the increased run distances, and can be decreased in number and duration if so desired as training progresses.

If you have more than 4 months before a marathon, the length of the LSD runs can be increased even more gradually. In that case, schedule the longest run you have planned three weeks before marathon day and work backwards from there until the first, and therefore shortest, LSD run occurs four weeks after you begin the programme. In addition to the Basic runs, do a LSD run once every three weeks – gradually increasing the distance/time – with a MD or Short Fast Distance (SFD)/Race run each other week (refer to the training programme plan).

Rest Days

Are just that. They are intended to give the body (and mind) a break from training so that it can replenish its energy stores and go about healing muscles or other structures that are sore from training. In the right proportion, rest days are as critical as training days. Other activities such as cycling, swimming or walking can be undertaken during these days if you don't like doing nothing at all. However, the intensity level should be kept very low, so that the activity is relaxing and enjoyable!

Training Programme Plan

The following plan is an overview of how to train in the four months leading up to a marathon. The marathon is scheduled at the end of Week 16, as they are usually held on a weekend. Each week is numbered and by looking to the right of the number you can see what sessions are to be planned into that week. There is also a copy of a training diary page at the back of this book so that the training sessions can be accurately monitored.

Times given (MD & LSD runs) are based on a 6 min/km pace (i.e.- it takes 6 minutes to complete 1km).

Week	Basic	SFD race	MD	LSD	Rest
1	3-4 x 30-45min		1 x 10 – 12km (1:00 – 1:12)		2-3 days
2	3-4 x 30-45min		1 x 13 – 15km (1:18 – 1:30)		2-3
3	3-4 x 30-45min	1 x 5km (20 – 30 min)			2-3
4	3-4 x 30-45min			1 x 16 – 20km (1:36 – 2:00)	2-3
5	3-4 x 30-60min		1 x 9 – 11km (0:54 – 1:06)		2-3
6	"""	1 x 5km (20 – 30min)			2-3
7	"""			1 x 20 – 25km (2:00 – 2:30)	2-3
8	"""		1 x 12 – 14km (1:12 – 1:24)		2-3
9	"""	1 x 5km (20 – 30min)			2-3
10	"""			1 x 25 – 29km (2:30 – 2:54)	2-3
11	"""		1 x 14 – 16km (1:24 – 1:36)		2-3
12	"""	1 x 5km (20 – 30min)			2-3
13	"""			1 x 29 – 32km (2:54 – 3:12)	2-3
14	3-4 x 30-50min		1 x 10km (1:00)		3-4
15	3-4 x 30-40min				3-4
16	2 x 30min & 2 short walks			*MARATHON	4

For example – you might organise Week 2 like this:

Mon	Tues	Weds	Thurs	Fri	Sat	Sun
Rest	35 min	45 min	45 min	30 min	1:18 – 1:30	Rest

This sort of routine worked well for me. I would increase the run lengths through the week, drop back to a shorter distance the day before a long run and then completely recover after it with one or two rest days. However, you may prefer (for example) one of the rest days to be more in the middle of the week, or to have three rest days instead of two. The long run shown on this Saturday is to last between 1 hour 18 minutes and 1 hour 30 minutes.

There are suggested times and distances listed under the MD and LSD runs. These times have been calculated on running at a 6 minute/km pace. If this pace is maintained, then the total time to run a marathon would be about 4:13 (4 hours 13 minutes). Slower paces of 6.5, 7 and 7.5 minutes per km would result in marathon times of around 4:34, 4:55, and 5:17 respectively. A faster pace of 5.5 min/km would equate to running a 3:52 marathon.

During the Rotterdam marathon our running time was displayed on big clocks at each 1km mark for the first 5km. At this early stage my pace was exactly 5.5min/km, and at the halfway point I had taken just under two hours. However my second 21km was slower than the first, and by the end of the 42.195km my time average over the whole run worked out to just under 6 minutes/km. An analysis of the official results showed that my first 5km were the fastest; my pace was the most constant from 10 to 20km (I had settled into a rhythm); and the last 5km leg was almost seven and a half minutes slower than my first 5km. Fatigue had well and truly set in! My official run time was 4:12, and is an achievement I am proud of. This was also in spite of my training schedule being disrupted on several occasions, which I discuss further in the coming chapters.

The times given in brackets for the MD and LSD runs in the programme are times that fit with **my** pace. Your times may differ from mine, so write your own times in for the planned distances when you become familiar with your pace. It is handy to have an idea of what your **running pace** is during the LSD training runs, so that you will have some idea of how long the marathon will take you. The way I did this was to note how long it took me to cover a certain part of my training run (5-10km) at what I thought my marathon pace would be. After the run I drove over that part in my car, noting the distance. Then I could figure out how fast I was running over that distance and work out my minutes per km pace. You could also work this out by timing yourself over a distance of several kilometres on an athletics track.

It is important to learn how to pace yourself over distance to maintain as even a pace as possible during the marathon. Starting out too fast – a common error – can result in not having the energy to go the whole distance. If you have an excess of energy, it is always better to speed up in the latter stages of the run than too early.

Rationale behind the training format

Now I'll explain some parts of the programme to clarify the logic behind it.

* The run times/distances have a degree of flexibility rather than being rigidly set.
  For example, a basic run of 30 to 45 minutes means that you can start low on 30 minutes and gradually build up to longer times, or start straight away with 45 minutes if that feels easy. If you're not an experienced long-distance runner there is no shame in having 30-minute training sessions. Keep in mind though that the aim is to build up from this time, so once training is going well incorporate more runs closer to 45 minutes than 30 minutes into the week.

* Week 1 – there is a MD run of at least 1 hour duration scheduled. It is a starting point for the longer runs you will build up to. As mentioned previously it is best if you already know how it feels to run for this long. The programme I followed wanted me to go around 19-22km for my first long run in Week 1, which equated to me running for a time of 1:55- 2:15. That was a big step for somebody used to regular 30-minute runs. The programme in this book leads more gradually to that level, with a run of 16-20km at Week 4.

* Weeks 2 & 3 – build on Week 1. There is also a SFD/Race run in Week 3, but nothing else longer than 45 minutes. This allows for some rest before the first LSD run in Week 4.

* Week 4 – now the real training begins! The first of four LSD runs before the marathon, this one is to be between 16 and 20km. With each such successive run 4 or 5km will be added to the maximum distance so that by Week 13 you will be running only a few kilometres less than the full marathon. There is a LSD run once every 3 weeks. In the other 2 weeks, apart from the basic runs there will only be a MD or SFD run. This gives the body a chance to recuperate from the stresses of the long runs. You should find that the

normal training runs seem much easier after the more difficult LSD ones.

* Week 5 – the basic runs have now been extended to 30-60 minutes, so you can choose longer runs as your stamina improves. There is also a MD run to be fitted in, but it is only half the distance of last week's LSD run.

* How do you decide which time to do on the LSD runs (if you're running by time)?
Let's say the programme shows you need to do one of between 1:36 and 2 hours. I found it best to aim for a middle time – say 1:48. Then you know that you've done more than the minimum suggested and you can go the full 2 hours if you're feeling good. Conversely, you can stop at around 1:36 if your body's had enough. You will know how long you want to run for as you get close to the end of the session. If I was feeling good I always tried to run for the longer time (refer also to "Knowing when to stop" in chapter 8 – Common Running Injuries).

* The last LSD run is scheduled 3 weeks before the marathon, to really allow for complete recovery. You might even feel better doing this run one week earlier, to allow 4 weeks between then and the marathon. This will depend on how quickly you recover from long runs. Closer to the marathon there are less and shorter runs, some walks and lots of stretching. The idea is that your injury-free body should feel energised, and hungry to do a long run again.

* There are either two or three rest days each week, and even up to four closer to the marathon. It is up to you how many you take each week based on how you are feeling. When training was going well for me I was taking one or two rest days, but injury (talked about later) put the overall average higher.

* Week 16 – by the week of the marathon you're hoping that nothing goes wrong in those last few days, so you take very good care of yourself. I wanted to feel like I had a surplus store of energy when I began the marathon, so I did very little training in that week. I did only two easy runs, and a couple of short, flat 15 to 30 minute walks so my muscles would not feel sluggish. The result was that I felt great going out from the start line.

Training Records

At the back of this book I have included **training diary** sample pages for your own training diary (enlarge the pages when you copy them). This should be filled in daily and is best done straight after each session while it is still fresh in your mind. But why keep a record at all?

A training diary is a summary of what you have done and felt during training. All serious athletes that I have known have kept some form of written record, and they can check back over many years for how they trained. The idea of this is to establish whether or not there are patterns – both beneficial and harmful – that may crop up from one season to another (or in shorter time spans). This enables you to evaluate your training progress and key happenings. For example, by looking back at records you will be able to read about how your training sessions went and how you felt just before you came down with an illness, so when you have similar feelings in the future you can suspect an approaching illness again. It is also useful to look back and see how injuries affected your progress; discover which workout schedules worked best for you; and be able to determine whether you over or under trained at certain times.

Perhaps one of the most important factors is being able, over time, to compare **competition preparations** to analyse which preparation training is most effective. This can include all aspects of competing – how you prepared physically, and mentally for a competition and even how you readied the equipment you had to use. For example, with cross-country skiing, different snow conditions require different waxes to be used on the ski base during classical-style races. By keeping a record of which ones did and did not work well in the different conditions, I could plan for a future race with a bit more ease of mind. Good wax choice meant the difference between the skis working with me during a race or having them make me feel like I was trying to run on ice!

A diary can act as a motivating factor. With the programme for this marathon, you have the workouts that need to be done each week. As one week ends it is a good idea to look at the following week's plan and write the workouts into the diary once you've decided what to do on which days (do it in pencil so that if necessary they can be swapped or altered). Then you can see exactly what you need to do for the week and you can prepare yourself mentally days ahead for the tougher workouts.

Even if you have never kept a diary before, I would strongly advise that you do for this marathon preparation. You really will benefit from looking back at training sessions to see what you need to do to make future ones easier. It is also a great record of the dedication you put into preparing for a wonderful sporting achievement!

Included in this chapter are two samples of diary pages. The first is a blank one so that you can see what my idea of a useful diary page is, and the second is a recorded example from my diary of the first marathon training LSD run I did. Take a look at the different headings in the blank page, then see what sort of information I filled in on my sample page, along with reading the following explanation.

Begin by putting a **date** on each session.

- **Day-Target** — this is where you write in what you plan to do for the day.

- **Morning HR** — what your resting heart rate reading is.

- **Run Route** — a description of where you ran. Handy when making time comparisons.

- **Distance/Time taken** — how far you actually ran and/or the time you took.

- **Date of last similar length run** — also useful for time and other comparisons.

- **Training Sort** — put a tick/cross next to the type of session.

- **Warm up/Cool down** — use ticks or comments for what you did.

- **Environment** — useful for checking back on the conditions you trained in, especially if looking for how they affected you.

- **Food/drink before training** — very important to make a note of these with the rehearsal runs to see what does and doesn't work well for you.

- **Time** — to determine how long you should leave between when you eat and when you begin training.

- **Session description** — especially in this part can you gain valuable insights into how your training is progressing. Here you can briefly describe the good and bad aspects of the session, and suggest improvements for future workouts. I always record how I felt the training went and how I coped physically and mentally. If

<u>WEEK   BEFORE MARATHON:</u>   Date:_____

Day   **Target:** _____
Morning HR: _____ beats/minute

Run Route: _____
_____
_____

Distance/Time taken:_____

Date of last similar length run:_____

Training sort: LSD_____**MD**_____ **Race/SFD**_____**Easy**_____
            Rest day_____ **Other(describe)**_____

Warm-up: stretches_____   **Cool down:**   stretches _____
            walk _____   walk _____
            jog _____   jog _____

Environment:

Time:_____ **Temperature:**_____ **Wind strength:**_____ **Rain?:**_____

Food/drink before training:_____

Time (between meal & training):_____

Session description:
Positive aspects:

Problems/how to improve:

Overall Rating:

☺👍_____   ☺_____   😐_____   ☹_____

fantastic   good   OK   not so good

My sample diary entry:
WEEK 11 BEFORE MARATHON: **Date:** 22/1/98
                                                  (in Australia)

Day 4 Target: 1:45 – 2 hrs
Morning HR: _54_____ beats/minute

Run Route: From home to pondage lake along highway, along back road to
Bee's corner and then return along same route

Distance/Time taken: 1:46 (1hr 46 mins) 19-20 km

Date of last similar length run: 1st longer run done

Training sort: LSD _x_ **MD**_____ **Race/SFD**_____ **Easy**_____
           Rest day_____ **Other(describe)**_____

Warm-up: stretches__x_____   **Cool down:**   stretches _a lot_____
                 walk_____x_____   walk ___x_____
                 jog _____x_____   jog _____

Environment:

Time: _7.00am_ **Temperature:** 20deg C **Wind strength:** light____ **Rain?:**_____

Food/drink before training: 1 slice toast & jam, 1 glass sports drink

Time (between meal & training): ___1 hour

Session description:
Positive aspects: Very happy with the time & distance I covered for my first
really long run. Ran pretty slowly. Measured distance in car later on – 10.4 km
one way.

Problems/how to improve: Had a slight stitch in the side at times, but not too
bad. Legs seemed a bit tired and sore even from early on – not enough stretching
after last w. out? Need to take some water along on the next long run.

Overall Rating:

fantastic   good   OK   not so good

something was not so good, then I would try to suggest what had caused the problem and how I could avoid it in the future.

◆ **Overall rating** – finally, a simple "tick the face", which corresponds to how happy you were with the session. When you are making comparisons in the future, it is a quick and easy way to see on which days you felt great or dreadful. Then you can read further into the day's description for more details. If there is a time when only the 'OK' and 'not so good' faces are being ticked, then it is possible your current training schedule or lifestyle may need evaluating. This will help determine what is adversely affecting the training sessions.

Chapter Two Summary

⇨ Determine your parameters for completing the marathon (run only; run/walk combination; goal time etc.).

⇨ Become familiar with the training terms used in this programme.

⇨ Slot the given workouts into your preferred days a week in advance (i.e. – each Sunday fill in the schedule for the week to follow).

⇨ Try to determine what your marathon pace will be.

⇨ Build gradually onto your run lengths.

⇨ Ensure there are enough rest days for adequate body recovery.

Chapter Three
Training Logistics

"Success is the sum of small efforts repeated day in and day out." – Robert Collier

Where and when to train

Having pleasant surroundings to train in definitely helps in coping with the many hours of training, but sometimes you can't be too choosy. If you live in a city then you might have to drive a bit to find some nice running areas, whereas if you're in the country you are often able to just step outside the door and start running. Fortunately I live in the suburbs of Rotterdam and I can run to a nearby nature area and then onto adjoining bike paths. Part of my circuit is on normal bitumen roads, but the traffic there is fairly light (I hate running alongside busy traffic with all the noise and exhaust fumes!). As the runs lengthen, you will need to find longer routes to train on – unless you enjoy doing the same shorter route several times. It was reasonably easy for me to keep following the never-ending bike paths as they wound themselves through parks and alongside a golf course. A golf course can actually be an excellent training ground, as long as the operators don't mind and you stick to the outer boundaries to avoid low flying missiles!

You might like to try joining a running club or find other local people also interested in marathon training so that you have company whilst training. Training alone or with a group is purely individual preference.

The preferred **time of day** to train varies between athletes, and is influenced by factors such as work demands. If you have your own business then you probably have more flexibility as to when you can train, but regular daytime employment often greatly reduces the time available for training. I prefer to train early in the morning. This gets me energised for the rest of the day, and I also know that I don't have to worry about training later on. But you may prefer training in the evening hours. It is a matter of determining when is best for you. I know athletes that run to work as part of their marathon training, or during lunchtimes, make themselves clamber out of bed extra early, or even run late at night to fit a session in. The point is that once you have committed yourself to experiencing a marathon, then you just have to keep following through with the training – it's called **"getting out of your comfort zone."**

Bad weather

I've had my fair share of training and competing in bad conditions over the years (when running, skiing etc.), and it is one of the things I enjoy least about competitive sport. You know that if you want the results you still have to get out and put in the preparation work. The same applies to marathon training. There is no guarantee that race day will be mild and sunny so you have to be prepared to run in any conditions. The best way to do that is to train in all sorts of weather. It's not so bad if it begins to rain during my run (falling snow is fun!), but it's always harder to make yourself start running if it is already raining. Of course there are people who like nothing better than running in rain! These are the times when you really need to focus on what you want to achieve in several weeks' time. Remind yourself that the discomfort is only temporary and that you'll be prepared whatever the marathon-day conditions are. Some days of constant torrential rain and gale force winds were just a bit too much to handle. Then I would usually turn to an indoor venue for some cross-training such as swimming, cycling or an aerobics workout.

When you are out in testing conditions, try to stay calm as getting frustrated and yelling obscenities into the wind doesn't usually alter the weather much (it's quite good for relieving tension though!). I can recall runs where I was barely moving forwards due to the gale force winds that are quite frequent in Holland – and all I could really do was laugh and think what good resistance training it was for my legs!

Marathon rehearsals

Just as you train in all weather to prepare, you can also treat each LSD run as an actual marathon rehearsal. These long runs are the ones that will let you know how your preparation is going and what you still need to work on. It is tempting to treat them like any other training runs, but if you make the extra effort to simulate all aspects of the marathon in those runs, you will be much better prepared physically and psychologically on the actual day.

Rehearsals can begin with the **days** you schedule your LSD runs. Most of these sessions I did on a Sunday, beginning around midday because that was the day of the week and time the marathon was scheduled for. At the end of the runs I would even try to feel as though I was finishing the marathon, and imagine how wonderful it would be. It's partly psychological training as well as physical – but every bit helps! An advantage to weekend training is that there is often more time free than during the week. Sometimes one of my planned LSD workouts could not happen on a weekend for one reason or another and then I usually ran it on the Monday instead. The beauty of this programme is that you can have such a degree of flexibility. Ensure that LSD sessions are not scheduled too close together though.

The **running surface** you train on should be similar to the marathon's surface. Prior to serious training for the marathon I ran quite a lot on soft grass or dirt paths, but I knew the race would be almost entirely on bitumen roads. I had to begin consciously choosing harder surfaces to train on. Changing from a softer surface to a harder one and at the same time increasing the distances run increases the risk of injuries such as shin splints, so add harder surfaces to your routine gradually.

One of the best reasons for rehearsing is to check out how your **running gear** performs. For LSD runs try to wear exactly what will be worn on the day. This includes the shoes, socks, underwear, shorts, shirt, and accessories such as sunglasses, hat and sweatband. When LSD training in bad weather, also wear the clothing you would wear during such conditions in the marathon. Clothing for the shorter training runs is not so important, but on the longer runs you will find out what is likely to cause you problems over 42.195km. I discovered problems like blisters caused by shoes and/or socks that were too loose, and chafing on the inner upper arms from my singlet (this can also occur on uncovered nipples). As you run longer your body will also let you know of any physical weaknesses. After a few runs I realised that the areas most likely to cause me problems would be my ankles and knees. By knowing this in advance I could at least try to avoid or minimise any problems (see Chapter 5).

To help minimise the risk of injury occurring during training, **warm-up** and **cool-down** periods should always be a part of the sessions. A warm-up consists of light activity that prepares the muscles for the training to follow. If muscles are warm then they are able to stretch and contract more effectively, and this reduces the risk of muscular injury. Stretching reduces muscle tension, which helps prevent the development of overuse injuries. Regardless of the type of training, I always do stretches beforehand as part of my warm-up (for 5 minutes or so). Then I walk a short distance before I begin running. For a SFD/race workout, you can also jog very easily for a few minutes as a warm-up before progressing to the faster pace. Sometimes during a run a particular muscle may feel 'over-tight'. It is a good idea to stop and do a stretch to make the muscle feel more relaxed. Otherwise the tightness may turn into a cramp or something more serious like a muscle tear.

A cool-down after the session is just as important and is meant to return the body functions gradually – rather than suddenly with an abrupt finish – to pre-exercise levels. My routine is usually to keep walking for a few minutes after finishing the run and then do another 5 to 10 minutes of stretching. Post-exercise walking will help the blood remove lactic acid from the body. This is a waste product which accumulates in the muscle cells during exercise and which causes muscle fatigue and post training soreness. Walking and stretching after training will help to minimise the amount of soreness you feel the next day (especially after a SFD/Race workout). It is very important in maintaining an injury-free training programme to take the few extra minutes each session to adequately warm-up and cool-down (refer to Chapter 12 for stretching suggestions).

Another essential part of rehearsing concerns what to **eat** and **drink**, and when (see also Chapter 6 – `What To Eat'). It is helpful to take note of how certain foods and drinks affect your training sessions. Often a morning run will feel slow for me if I have eaten a heavy meal the night before. Try to figure out what is best for your body by varying the types of food and drinks ingested and also the times between the meal and training (and keeping a written record). The night and morning before LSD runs eat as you would before the marathon – that means thinking about what your pre-marathon meals will consist of well ahead of time.

I experimented with sucking on some **energy (glucose) sweets** during the LSD runs. I kept them in a small flat pouch that velcroed on around my wrist. Whenever I wanted a tablet I unzipped the wallet and took one out. I also took some with me into the marathon. It is probably not a good idea to eat sugar or glucose tablets in the earlier stages of a marathon because although they will raise your blood sugar levels, this is only temporary. Later on an 'insulin-type' reaction can occur, where the levels will quickly fall, leading to early fatigue. However, I was happy to have some in the final stages of my run – even if the benefit was more of a psychological than physical one!

The body can generally rely on its energy stores for between 1 and 2.5 hours of exercise, depending on the exercise intensity and duration, and how full the body's carbohydrate (CHO) stores are. It is a safe bet that the marathon will take you longer than this to complete, so you will need some **CHO replacement** during the event. This can be achieved by eating CHO during the run (e.g. bananas or an energy bar) but it is more convenient instead to ingest the appropriate sports energy drink usually provided. If you decide to eat as well as drink, then this definitely needs to be tried out during your training sessions so that it is a process familiar to you.

There is another reason for rehearsing taking drinks during the LSD sessions. Body moisture that is lost through sweat and exhaled air during training must continually be replaced with water or sports drinks, otherwise **dehydration** will occur. This affects the circulatory system, increases body temperature and heart rate, and causes fatigue and a decrease in performance.

Dehydration is observed most during events run in high temperatures when water is lost more rapidly from the body, but will occur any time body fluids are not adequately replenished. Checking during the day that your urine is pale in colour is an easy way to ensure your body is properly hydrated. Avoid consuming drinks containing caffeine – such as coffee, tea or alcohol close to, during or straight after training. Due to the caffeine they are actually diuretics which cause the body to lose water. So if you enjoy a beer after training, make sure that you have several glasses of water first!

If not monitored, dehydration can lead to more serious conditions such as heat exhaustion or heat stroke. It is worth looking at these two conditions in more detail, as marathon runners are often at particular risk of experiencing them.

Heat exhaustion can be caused by either dehydration or salt depletion in the body. Symptoms of both forms include weakness, distress, fatigue, thirst, dizziness, headache, nausea and vomiting, and may lead to collapse. Treatment for heat exhaustion consists of taking the athlete to a cool place and giving him/her water and electrolyte drinks.

Heat stroke is considered a medical emergency as the resulting high body core temperature (often higher than 41 degrees C) can be potentially fatal. Initial symptoms are similar to those for heat exhaustion, but in addition there are chills, goose-bumps, hyperventilation, muscle cramps, poor co-ordination, staggering, and incoherent speech. This can progress to unconsciousness and result in multiple organ failure and death. Heat stroke requires immediate medical treatment. Athletes must attempt to prevent heat stroke by avoiding dehydration, not running in high extremes of temperature or humidity, and not drinking alcohol before running. I'll always remember watching on television the heart wrenching sight of Gabriel Anderson-Scheiss, barely managing to crookedly stagger through the last metres of an Olympic marathon before collapsing over the finish line. She had obviously suffered from extreme exertion and dehydration, and required medical aid after the finish.

During a marathon there are usually regularly spaced **drink stations** (every 5km or so) offering a variety of fluids like water and sport drinks. If possible, find out which sports drink will be used so you can get used to it in training. The specially formulated sports drinks – such as Gatorade, Extraan Isostar, Staminade, etc. – generally consist of mineral salts and glucose polymers in solution. These are intended respectively to replace body salts lost in sweat, and provide some carbohydrate energy to the body during intense exercise. The body salts are needed for specific cellular functions and the CHO component can help to delay the onset of exhaustion, which is especially helpful in the latter stages of a marathon.

In a marathon it is not uncommon for runners to experience a state of exhaustion somewhere around the 30-35km mark and it is known as **'hitting the wall'** (the Dutch equivalent is 'meeting the man with the hammer!'). The symptoms include feeling tired, weak and lethargic, getting cramps, and it becomes difficult to keep running. Some of the causes can include – running too fast early on in the race, overheating, low blood sugar levels, and dehydration. This emphasises the points of ensuring that you maintain a high CHO diet prior to the marathon for good glycogen fuel stores in the muscles and liver (see Chapter 6), not starting out too quickly, and staying well hydrated during the run.

In the '98 Rotterdam marathon there were drink but no food stations, to limit the chance of participants having stomach upsets. On the longer rehearsal runs take a cycling bidon (plastic bottle) filled with water or a dilute sports drink with you (sports drinks that are too concentrated can cause stomach upsets). You can buy bottle carriers that strap on snugly around the waist. Practise taking a few mouthfuls every fifteen to twenty minutes. Don't wait until you feel thirsty to have a drink, as the dry mouth feeling usually means the body has already begun to dehydrate. I trained with a cordial mixture (water and syrup) but during the marathon had some of the sports drinks. I ended up getting a slight stitch in the side at one stage, so reverted back to plain water drinks in case the unfamiliar electrolytes in the sport drink had caused the problem. The stitch did go away. The main point is to be familiar with all aspects of the marathon.

Running technique

Running styles can be as varied as the runners themselves, and if you feel comfortable with how you run then keep that technique. There are some basics to keep in mind though. Because the marathon is a duration event the body needs to be kept as relaxed as possible. Every muscle that is unnecessarily tensed uses up energy that should be saved for use by the running muscles. Sprinters pump their arms vigorously over short distances to help with speed, but this is not necessary in a marathon (unless you're charging for the finish line!). Keep the arms relaxed and held at a comfortable height, with fists unclenched. Every now and then during the run you can also shake your arms out straight to release tension built up from them being held in the same position. Relax the facial muscles and keep a steady breathing rhythm.

Hills can pose a problem if you're not used to running them, and if there are significant hills in your marathon it is important to run some during training. It is much easier to continue smoothly up hills rather than struggle up them, gasping for breath at the top. The idea with distance running is to establish a regular running rhythm. When confronted with a hill, simply aim to maintain that rhythm. To do this, lean forward a bit and take smaller steps as you start to climb so that your footsteps are making the same rhythm sound as when you are running on the flat. Trying to take the same size steps up a hill as on the flat will mean that you need to expend more energy, and this means having to start breathing harder to get more air. Your breathing should be able to stay at the same rhythm going uphill if your steps are smaller – it's just like changing down gears on a bike as you start climbing. Feel that you are not putting any more effort into your uphill steps than what you would on the flats. Once you reach the top of a hill then gradually lengthen your stride again. If you have a steep descent during a run (usually more common in cross-country runs) it is best to hold back a bit with your steps rather than letting your legs go full pelt out of control. The latter can be too severe on the joints and muscles, and increases the risk of falling or spraining an ankle.

Stress monitoring

A good athlete knows how to listen to and interpret his/her body's signals – to determine when training can be intensified or when there is a need to back off for a while. There will be some days when you really don't feel like training, and it is important to understand why. It could simply be a matter of not wanting to go out into bad weather conditions, but on the other hand your body might be trying to signal something more serious.

I remember a biathlon race I took part in one winter. It was a state title and we had to ski 10km, stopping between loops to shoot at the range. I was only about 2km into the race and feeling so drained of energy that I considered stopping. I had never pulled out of a race before and it was a real mental struggle for me as I tried to figure out whether or not I should push myself to keep going. The next hill seemed like Mount Everest, so reluctantly I pulled out. I had no symptoms of any sickness, and I was hoping the coach believed me when I said I couldn't understand what had gone wrong. The next day my resting heart rate was much higher than usual and so I felt I should go to my doctor for some blood tests. Sure enough the results came back that I had been attacked by a 24-hour virus, and my body's energy stores had been busy fighting off the intruders instead of helping me win a ski race!

Resting heart rate is often a good indicator of how training is going. Typically, as a body becomes fitter, the resting heart rate will become lower. At my fittest with ski training my lowest recorded HR was 42 beats per minute (b/m), but there are accounts of athletes with recorded heart rates as low as 30 b/m. The average untrained adult usually has a resting HR of between 60-75 b/m.

The idea is to take and record your pulse rate each morning, so that over time you can see if it deviates from the normal reading, figure out why and if necessary, adjust your training accordingly. Heart rate is best taken first thing in the morning before you get out of bed. The easiest way to check it is to locate the pulse in your wrist artery (on the thumb side) or on a throat artery (slide fingers up alongside the voice box to the top of the throat and press gently). Use the first two fingers and not the thumb, as the thumb has a pulse of its own and can confuse the reading. To get a per minute reading, count the pulses for one minute using a watch for starting and stopping. Over a few days you can see what your average resting HR figure is.

You can also take your HR at the end of training sessions (and during) to compare over time. It is better to count the pulses over 10 seconds (rather than 1 minute) and then multiply the number by 6 for a per minute reading. This is because once you stop running your HR will drop quickly as you recover, so the shorter recording time will give a more accurate training HR figure. It takes some concentration to get an accurate reading if your heart is racing though! I take my pulse after most runs, and I usually find that if a session has felt a bit more difficult than usual then my after-training heart rate is often higher as well. It's interesting to know how different training sessions compare.

If on awaking, your resting HR figure is five or more beats above the usual, then this can indicate one of several things. It may mean that you are coming down with a cold or some other **sickness**, and your body systems are working harder to overcome the problem. It could also indicate a **lack of sleep, emotional stress** or an overly **hard training** session the day before. In such a case the body is signalling that it needs more rest. This is one reason why it is a good idea to plan one or more rest days or very easy workouts straight after your harder LSD/Race sessions. Try to avoid doing hard workouts on two consecutive days, as the body needs adequate time to recover after the first session.

Going to a place of higher **altitude** than you are used to will result in an increased heart rate for the first few weeks of training, until you are acclimatised. This is something to keep in mind if you are entering a marathon that is held in a mountainous area! Running in high **temperatures** can also cause an increase in training heart rate as the body works harder to stay cool.

Taking a few days off training due to minor **illnesses** will not be a setback to your fitness, but training when you are ill can be worse for you than if you had rested. If you're not feeling too well when you wake up and your heart rate is higher than usual, take a rest day or plan to do a modified run, something shorter and slower than usual. If you feel really drained after a few minutes into the run, then just stop and walk. There is no sense in pressuring yourself to train when your body is not up to it. Learn to listen to your body and understand its signals. I know that if I wake up with the symptoms of a mild common cold (slightly sore throat, sniffles and sneezing), then I benefit more from going for a short, easy run or cycle than if I'd done nothing. However, if it is anything more serious then I will rest until I feel able to train effectively again. Under no circumstances should you train with a fever, as training will increase the already high body temperature, with possible serious consequences. If you're not sure whether a specific condition should stop you from training, consult a doctor or other qualified practitioner.

Training too hard for too long can lead to a condition of chronic fatigue, also known as **burnout** or **over-training.** A cumulative condition, it can last for days or even months. The symptoms of over-training include feelings of general tiredness, irritability and lethargy, a susceptibility to colds, and not wanting to train. The best solution is to take time off from the regular training scheme to give the body and mind a chance to "recharge". That may be for a few days or a few weeks, but the goal is to build up the mental and physical enthusiasm for running again. Do some completely different activities during that time. Continuing with heavy training when fatigued will only worsen the condition and increase the risk of injury. Also, friends and associates might get sick of being around a grumpy person!

Training Tips

* Train at the same time each day if possible to establish a routine.
* Try to have some different run routes for variety.
* If you're feeling stale with the same old training, do something completely different for a session or two (swimming, cycling, inline skating, parachuting.....).
* Do an easy workout before a LSD run and have at least one rest day after it.
* Don't schedule a race day close to a LSD run.
* A day you have to travel somewhere can be scheduled ahead of time as a rest day.
* Wear comfortable clothing (does not have to be fashionable or expensive!).
* Don't over dress, as you will heat up quickly when running.
* Wear sunglasses on sunny and/or windy days.
* A baseball cap can help keep rain off your face on wet days.
* Double knot your shoelaces so that they don't come undone during the run.
* I don't brush my teeth before running as I find my mouth becomes very dry.

- Sometimes you don't feel like going for a run because you think it will be slow or hard. Go anyway, as sometimes these turn out to be the best ones!

- If the run is feeling really bad, or you experience sharp pain somewhere, stop.

- Run towards dogs cautiously — some like to chase moving objects.

- Avoid standing on dog poop — it really sticks into your shoe tread!

- Be enthusiastic about your training — appreciate the fact that you are healthy enough to be able to train with a special goal in mind.

Chapter Three Summary

⇨ Follow your plan as closely as possible, regardless of weather conditions.

⇨ Use the LSD sessions to mimic what you envisage yourself doing in the marathon.

⇨ Rehearsals refer to technique, what you wear (see Chapter 4), and what you drink and eat beforehand and during the run.

⇨ Be aware of dehydration during training.

⇨ Know how heat exhaustion and heat stroke occur and how their occurrences can be minimised.

⇨ Always include a warm-up and cool-down in each session.

⇨ Train on similar terrain to what you will experience in the marathon.

⇨ Resting heart rate can help monitor training progress.

⇨ A higher than usual resting H.R can be a warning sign.

⇨ Learn to listen to and understand your body's signals.

⇨ Be cautious about training when ill.

⇨ Fill in the training diary daily after each session.

⇨ Use the diary information to aid you in future training sessions.

⇨ Approach training sessions in a positive frame of mind.

⇨ **Enjoy yourself!**

Chapter Four

Clothing

"Don't judge runners by their coverings!"

Clothes for daily training

Many sports stores now stock a large selection of designer running attire to suit every fashion taste. Clothing of all colours,
styles and fabrics will tempt you to look trendy when you run. If
you don't mind spending money then even if you can't perform
like a world-class athlete, at least you can look like one!

For **daily** training sessions, choose comfortable, non-restric-
tive clothing. Leggings, lycra bike shorts or a one piece catsuit
are all good because they don't flap around. They are especially
suitable for runners with large thighs because they prevent the
problem of chafing. If you don't like anything restrictive around
the waist, elastic tops on shorts and leggings can be turned down
a fold to rest on the hips. Choose underwear that fits well and
doesn't go creeping all over the place when you run.

In warm weather I wear a singlet on short runs and a light
T-shirt for longer runs as the singlet armholes can chafe on the
upper arms over a long distance. When buying a running top,
check the fabric type and cut under the armpit to assess if they
could lead to chafing. If the morning is a bit cool then I also wear
a lightweight long-sleeved top.

When the weather turns really **cold** (less than 5 degrees Celsius) with wind, rain and/or snow, then it's time to rug up more.
Thermal underwear is good as a bottom layer as it maintains
body warmth and also absorbs sweat. This can usually be purchased at outdoor sports shops. Over that goes a pair of tracksuit
pants, a T-shirt and a light windproof jacket. A jacket made of
Gore-Tex fabric can be expensive, but the "breathable"
Gore-Tex allows for good air circulation. A couple of storage
pockets are handy in case you want to take a hat or gloves off
part way through the run. Use a thin woollen hat, thick sport
socks and thin gloves to protect extremities. On frosty mornings
a scarf wrapped around the neck and sitting loosely in front of

the mouth helps to take the chill out of each breath, which is especially useful if you are susceptible to coughs. A baseball cap is good for keeping rain out of the eyes, but needs to fit snugly to stay on in strong winds.

After training in cold or rainy conditions it is important not to stand around getting colder. This can lower the body's resistance to certain illnesses, so make sure to get warm and dry again as soon as possible. If the body core temperature drops too far (to 35 degrees C or less) from prolonged exposure to the cold, then **hypothermia** occurs. Symptoms of this condition include severe shivering, weakness, irritability and poor co-ordination. With a further drop in body temperature this can progress to delirium, coma and death.

Prevention of hypothermia includes wearing adequate clothing for the conditions and avoiding the consumption of alcohol before and during activity (as it dilates the blood vessels, leading to increased heat loss from the body). Mild forms can be treated by dressing the athlete in dry, warm clothes in a warm environment, but more severe cases will require medical treatment.

What will I wear during the marathon?

The answer is just what you have worn when rehearsing the marathon in your LSD runs. By marathon day you should know what feels comfortable and works. What you wear will affect how comfortably you run the distance, and clothing should not be causing problems that you have to be thinking about during the run.

Not being too concerned with appearances I relied on the familiar training clothes I knew worked well. That meant some bike shorts and a very light 12-year-old T-shirt (knotted at the middle to look trendier!). When I began training for the marathon I bought special pairs of running socks (cost about $20). They had extra padding at the heel and under the ball of the foot and contained an elastic material to prevent them slipping down. Comfortable to wear, I used them in all my LSD runs. Alternatively you may not wish to wear socks at all, but the feeling was too strange for me when I tried sock-less running sessions.

It can be fun trying on and buying sleek-looking running clothes, but aim to possess a functional all-weather selection.

Train with the same clothes you will use in the marathon to become familiar with them.

Accessories

There are several other items that can be useful when running. Many athletes wear a **watch** that has a stopwatch built into it. This is handy if you want to be accurately timing your runs. A **sweatband** worn around the wrist and/or forehead is a good idea if you sweat a lot. On sunny days a **baseball hat** and/or **sunglasses** will decrease the amount of glare on your eyes. If your hair is long enough to get into your eyes or mouth on windy days, then putting your hair into a ponytail and wearing a **hairband**/sweatband will minimise this annoyance. A **bidon** container of drink worn around the waist is a must to guard against dehydration. You may even decide you want to wear it during the marathon if you want drinks more often than the organised stations will be supplying them. Mentioned in Chapter 3, I also found it useful to wear a small, light **pouch** which velcroed on around the wrist. In it I carried some unwrapped glucose tablets, which definitely helped me through the last stages of the race. A pouch can also be used to hold keys or loose coins.

At this stage there is only one main item of clothing still to be discussed.

Running Shoes

Another important aspect to your marathon success is the type of shoes you run in. Over the years I have trained in several different brands of running shoe, and once you find one you like you want to stay with them forever. I never really knew if they were good or not for my anatomical structure, but if they were comfortable then that was enough. In the very first half-marathon I ran as a teenager, I wore a pair of tennis shoes with a completely flat sole and no cushioning. It was a great run and because I didn't know better, the shoe type never entered my mind (I didn't feel like I'd sustained any physical damage anyway!). I also remember running around the school oval endlessly at lunchtimes to become a member of the 50km club – healthy enough, but if I forgot my sports shoes then I just ran in flat sandals. Maybe it is no coincidence that I now wear orthotics (specialised moulded shoe inserts) to compensate for slightly flat feet! Orthotics are something that I had to get used to with running, but now they present no problem. Many people do need to use orthotics due to irregularities in foot structure. However it is good to see that aspiring runners now have access to a greater choice of appropriate running shoes, and staff who are knowledgeable about those shoes.

With the huge variety of shoes available it can be difficult to know which sort to buy. Shoe companies now develop ranges of shoes for all sorts of different activities, so a shoe suited to one type of sport may not give you the support you need when participating in another sport. As I was forced to try different types over the years (because of a discontinued model etc.), I became aware of what I specifically wanted and which brands did not provide the support I needed. There is one popular brand that I cannot wear, because as soon as I put those shoes on, my feet sink inwards so that I feel like a duck when I walk!

Fashion and functionality

Without proper knowledge, you may not even be aware that the shoes you train in are actually causing problems. This turned out to be the case for me in at least one instance. For a number of years I happily trained in a common brand of runner that seemed to function well. In actual fact they were responsible for me feeling a dull ache in my knees. Sometimes you will experience a slight nagging feeling in a muscle or joint that although annoying, doesn't stop you from training – you just put up with it. In my case there would almost always be the same sort of feeling in my knees at some stage during training sessions. I just put it down to doing too much hill training during my competitive skiing days and didn't let it worry me.

One day we went to a shoe specialist to get some runners for Mart, but I didn't intend buying any myself. Once there, I asked the specialist about my choice of training shoe. He said that he never recommended them to serious athletes as he had heard of them being associated with some knee problems. I wondered if they could be my problem and even though they were still fairly new, I went ahead and bought a pair of women's Asics Gel runners to try out. My first session with them was just after it had rained, so they didn't stay new looking for very long (why do they put so much white on women's runners?). But more importantly it was my first run for a long time that was completely discomfort-free. I was amazed to find that the Asics allowed me to run without the previous discomfort I had experienced in my knees. It just goes to show that it is a question of finding the right shoe to fit your running style.

It is worth spending the money to have the brand of running shoe that suits you, and taking the time to get advice from specialists who really know what they are talking about. If they have the proper computer equipment they will also be able to give you an analysis of your walking/running technique, to show which parts of your foot are subjected to the most pressure. Then they can recommend the best type of shoe for you and tell you how often you should buy new ones, based on the amount of training you are doing. Marathon runners often buy new shoes after training in them for between 1500 to 2000km. Another advantage to **technical analysis** is that the detection of physical abnormalities (such as flat feet) at this stage can help prevent anatomically related injuries occurring further on down the track (see Chapter 8 – Injuries).

Whichever type of running shoes you use, make sure they are worn in well before doing a marathon with them – but not to the worn out stage. New shoes can often lead to blisters forming somewhere on the feet for the first few times they are used. Once worn in a little there shouldn't be a problem. But if you wear brand new shoes on the day of the marathon – that's asking for trouble! Getting blisters in the first few kilometres of the run is not something that makes for a pleasant experience (you'll be surprised though how many people do turn up with brand new shoes on!). It's a good idea to buy a suitable pair of new shoes when you begin this training programme, and use them in training and during the marathon.

There are a different number of ways you can lace up shoes. A shoe specialist can show you the most effective way, but in the end I just went with what I was most comfortable with. I prefer using flat laces to round ones, as the round ones always seemed to come undone part way through the runs unless they were double knotted. It is important to pay attention to how tightly you lace up your shoes. At one stage I laced my shoes too tightly before a LSD run and ended up with an inflamed tendon on the top of my foot (discussed further in "Complications", Chapter 5). Make sure that the shoe fits snugly, not too loose or tight.

Having the right pair of running shoes plays an important part in your marathon success, but keep in mind that the price tag on the shoe does not necessarily reflect the true value of the shoe. Of course if you're on a really tight budget, you can wear something like what the slowest Rotterdam 1999 beginner did – clogs! (I never did learn if he made it the entire way!).

Tips to Get the Right Shoes

+ Preferably, buy shoes from a specialist, and even better is one who also runs marathons.

+ Take your current training shoes along when buying new ones so that the shoe specialist can see by the tread wear how you run.

+ If you have problems with injuries, make sure to mention them.

+ Wear the type of socks you train in when purchasing new shoes.

+ Avoid buying shoes that are too tight – it is usually better to buy looser than tighter.

+ Check that the heel counter is supportive and not weak.

+ Check for sufficient padding under the front of the foot.

+ Make sure that the sole is flexible as opposed to rigid.

+ Purchase the correct type of shoe for what you want to do.

+ Ensure that the shoes are wide enough for comfortable foot and toe movement.

* While the most expensive shoes are not necessarily the best, cheap shoes often wear out quickly and contribute to injury. Choose your shoes carefully.

Chapter Four Summary

⇨ Training clothes need to allow a free range of movement.

⇨ Dress for training according to the weather conditions.

⇨ Decide which clothes will be worn in the marathon.

⇨ Determine if special running clothes or shoes need to be purchased.

⇨ Buy clothing well before the marathon so that you can also train in it.

⇨ Think about obtaining running accessories that might be useful.

⇨ Leg pain could be a sign that you are not wearing suitable shoes.

⇨ Consider getting advice on running shoes from a shoe specialist.

⇨ Check training shoes regularly for wear and replace them well before they become detrimental to performance.

⇨ Never wear brand new shoes in a marathon (or clogs?).

Chapter Five
Complications Along the Way

"It's not the mountain that will stop you, but the stone in your shoe." – R.W. Service

Achieving goals is not always an easy process, and completing a marathon is no exception. If it were an easy thing to do, then everybody would be able to do it. Part of the marathon's attraction lies in having to push your limits to succeed. You may also find that during the preparation training there will be times when things don't seem to be going to plan. This chapter focuses on a few of the problems I had along the way and what I did about them – you may even be familiar with some of them!

Away from home

One advantage of a planned training programme is being able to get into a routine. You know when and where to train and how long it takes to run different circuits. This can alter completely if you need to spend time away from your training area. It is most difficult when that place is unfamiliar to you, and you don't know your way around at all. However, there is no need to wait until you get very used to the area before beginning to train there. Running around the new location is one of the best ways to become familiar with the area. Using a bicycle to initially orient yourself can be a fun way to get a fix on things. Talking to other local runners who can give advice on where to train is also another avenue of learning about the area.

If you have to travel for the better part of a day, then work this day into your plan as a rest day. It feels particularly good if you have done a hard workout the day before travelling. When you are at the new destination take some time to go for a drive around the area to look for a suitable running route. Check out if there is a golf course, park or forest area nearby that you could run around. A foolproof method of not getting lost is simply to run in as straight a line as possible for half of the required training time, then run back again. As long as you don't take any turns, then you shouldn't get lost.

Getting a stitch

A stitch is an annoyance I have experienced on many occasions during training sessions, and I have tried all sorts of things to avoid them. A stitch presents itself as a sharp pain in the side, and is commonly felt at the bottom edge of the ribcage, in my case always on the right hand side.

Stitches seem to occur randomly. At times I will have a mild stitch that comes and goes during a run, other days I'll have one that stays for the whole distance, and yet in other sessions they do not bother me at all. It doesn't seem to matter whether I do an easy or a race session, a stitch might be present or absent during either.

Over time I have tested a number of "anti-stitch" strategies. I concentrated on changing my **breathing technique,** altered the amounts of **food and drink** I consumed before training and also how much **time** I left between eating and training. I also noticed that I often kept my lower abdomen tensed when running, instead of letting it move in and out with my breathing rhythm, which is also referred to as "belly breathing". As you breathe in the belly should move out, and vice versa so that your breathing rhythm is even and relaxed (as taught in yoga classes). This abdominal tensing seemed to be one way I could cause a stitch to form.

I tried running on an empty stomach versus having something to eat prior to training and it seemed that I was more prone to getting a stitch if I ran without first eating something. I don't enjoy running with a heavy feeling in my stomach, so I would just have something light and there didn't need to be much time between eating and training. For the longer runs I would leave at least a one-hour period between eating and running. Diet is discussed in more detail in Chapter 6.

I also noticed that I was more likely to experience a stitch if I had done a hard sit-ups workout at the gym the night before. Another likely scenario was if I tried to push a 'burp' out. If you have the urge to burp whilst running, then let the air out but without tensing the abdominal muscles. Simply open your throat a little wider and let the air slide on out without altering your breathing rhythm.

It seems likely that there is a connection (for me anyway) between having a stitch and how tense the abdominal muscles are, and perhaps the diaphragm is also linked to the equation (the respiratory muscle between the chest and abdomen). I mention the diaphragm because if you do experience a stitch, one of the ways to make it go away is to dig your fingers into the painful spot under the ribs and up into the diaphragm. This pressure often relieves the pain and you can keep running. However, a stitch can recur at a later stage.

When you press your fingers into the site of the stitch, I have found that it helps to bend over from the waist at the same time. This helps relieve tension in the affected muscle and if it is not a very painful stitch, then you can manage to do this whilst continuing to run. If the stitch is sharp then it is better to stop and try the procedure. Recommence running slowly. Another avenue you can try (especially if one occurs during a fast session) is to slow your pace down. This often also removes the stitch and you can gradually speed up again.

I have also found that I am more prone to getting a stitch when recommencing training after having had time off due to injury etc. In this case the stitches occur less frequently after a few weeks of running again.

Injuries

There is a whole chapter devoted to injuries runners commonly experience, but I wanted to relate here the particular problems I developed during my marathon preparation, and what I did to overcome them.

Knee lock

This unusual experience occurred not long after I began the training programme. After a short session (6km or so) I did my usual cool-down, changed clothes then sat down behind the computer to do some work. I was busy for probably a couple of hours then got up to do something else. The problem was that I felt a pain almost like a cramp in my knee joint, and I wasn't able to put weight on it normally. That night I had to sleep with my legs straight, as any effort to bend them caused pain in the affected knee.

There was no question of running the following day, or for

several days after. I wore a supportive elastic knee band that completely covered and extended above and below the knee joint, and that enabled me to at least walk around without too much trouble. After the first couple of days I went for slow walks instead of running. Gradually the pain and stiffness went away and I was able to recommence running on the sixth day after it first happened.

The only reason I could think of for this happening was that I sat in one position for too long immediately after finishing training. My legs were bent under the chair for the time I was working on the computer, and it seemed like the connective structures in that knee joint somehow "locked up". I now have a footstool under the computer table so that I can keep my legs straight. Happily there has been no recurrence of this nasty incident.

Torn muscle

I experienced a major setback to training during a LSD run in the fifth week. Until then I had kept to the schedule set for me and in Week 3 had completed one LSD run of 1:46 (19-20km), which I was reasonably happy with. The next aim was to run for 2:15-2:30, so, in Australia at the time, I began at 6.30am to avoid the summer heat. I also wore a peaked cap and sunglasses and carried a bottle of water. The route through town took me along bitumen and dirt roads and then I continued on a grass golf course (some of the courses in drier towns are comprised of red dirt with 'greens' of sand!). I was drinking water along the way and was feeling pretty good at 1:16, which is when I incurred an injury. My training diary comments for the day read: `Going quite well until I felt a sudden sharp pain in my lower left calf. Had to walk back from the golf course. Pretty disappointing. No stitch though (always find something positive!). Blister on my right heel.'

The muscle tear in the middle of my lower left calf really came as a surprise. I had been running comfortably mentally and physically, and being over halfway was heading for home again. The pace was relaxed and it all happened from one instant to the next, as if someone had suddenly stuck a knife into my calf muscle. Being optimistic I was hoping it was just a bad cramp, so after walking for a bit I tried to run again. No way – that calf wasn't going to let me run another step further!

Later I tried to figure out why it had happened. It wasn't that the distance was too long, as I had already run a half-hour longer in Week 3. Maybe I hadn't stretched enough prior to beginning, but the pace was so easy that it shouldn't have been a problem. Maybe it was caused by the grassy surface, or another thought that comes to mind is that just before it happened I remember thinking how good I was feeling. It is possible that I then tried to pick up the pace for the second half, which may have suddenly over-stressed the muscle too much.

The amount of recovery time needed, will depend on how severe an injury is. If you begin training again too early, then you are likely to have a repeat occurrence of the same injury – which can set you back for longer than if you had let it heal properly in the first place. I didn't go to a specialist because being accustomed to sustaining different injuries over the years, I was certain it was a simple muscle tear.

I didn't train for the next two days and then started slow 20 or so-minute walks each day. Eight days after being injured I ran for a total of 10 minutes, in three stages of 4, 4 and 2 minutes, with walking in between. The surface was a flat earthen track. I was still aware of the injury site hurting, but I've always been a firm believer in gently pushing the limits to get back into training as soon as possible (approach cautiously). To help prevent scar tissue forming during the healing process, I massaged and stretched the muscle each day.

In the next five days I did three runs of between 8 and 13 continuous minutes. The following day I was able to run for 20 minutes and it was the first run in which the calf hadn't felt sore. Finally! Two days later I was back to 45 minutes, and then three days after that I was up to 1:20. From the day of the injury to the first pain-free 20 minutes I had lost two and a half weeks of scheduled training.

In such a situation there is nothing you can do but rest, allow the injury to heal (with the proper rehabilitative treatment) and hope that the same problem doesn't occur close to marathon day. During future LSD runs I was worried that the muscle might tear again, but I didn't have any further problem with that muscle.

Inflamed tendons and blisters

Being a little careless at times can lead to a problem that really did not need to occur in the first place. There is a saying that `experience is the best teacher', but it's much smarter to hear and learn about the painful experiences from someone else than to have to go through them yourself!

In Week 8 I did a LSD run of about 2:00. During the run I noticed some extra pressure on the top of my right foot because of laces tied a bit too tightly, but fixated on my watch and the path ahead, I didn't want to stop running to retie them. By the end of the run I could also feel some soreness in my calf muscles, knees and hips. When I commenced the following training run I quickly noticed that the foot tendon was quite painful and the only way I could relieve it was to have the laces tied loosely. So, **if something is causing you discomfort during a training session, where possible, take the time to stop and fix it.** If I had have stopped and retied my laces properly during the LSD run then I probably wouldn't have had the subsequent tendon injury. It sounds silly, but sometimes you just want to keep running regardless of what is going on around you. (I noticed that in the same but newer model of Asics shoe I purchased late in 1998, they have helped minimise this problem by making the shoe tongue much thicker and better padded.)

One problem of running with loose shoes is that all sorts of grit and dirt gets flicked into them, and this does not make for comfortable running. The more obvious problem is that your foot is not being supported as it should be, which can lead to even more injuries. Not wanting to stop training I decided to try using some padding. I took a circular cotton pad and cut a hole in the middle of it, then placed it on the foot with the hole over the tendon. The idea was to keep pressure off the sore tendon. This actually worked quite well, but it still took two weeks for the inflammation and pain to disappear. A variety of such pads can be bought ready-made from chemist and sports stores. A sports physiotherapist might have suggested that I also use a suitable anti-inflammatory cream.

Another problem of running with loose shoes (or socks) is that blisters can readily form. This is due to the continuous friction of the loose shoe and/or sock against the heel or another foot part.

The bubble of fluid that forms just under the skin's surface in response to the friction is called a blister. Once a blister has formed then any pressure on that spot will be painful, which can temporarily hinder training.

Due to the extra distance covered in a LSD run, I found that at times **blisters** would form on my outer toes. To help prevent this I put a couple of plasters around them before any future runs and that seemed to help greatly. I have found that the best treatment for a blister is to make a small hole in it with a sterile needle and gently push the fluid out. Then cover it with a plaster to keep it dry and clean against infection. The only time I experienced heel blisters was when I had to have the shoe tied loosely, or when I was running in a new pair of shoes for the first few times.

More knee trouble

During a 2:30 LSD run, I noticed that my left inner knee became quite sore from about the 2-hour mark onwards. I felt it again in my next short run after 25 minutes, so stopped to walk the rest of the way. After that it seemed to be fine again. However, four and a half weeks before the marathon I ran for 2:45 and the second half of the run was dreadful, in that half my knee would start to twinge, I would stop and massage it and then I could run for about 6 minutes before having to repeat the process. On top of that my inner ankles were also sore and my right calf muscle started cramping in the last 15 minutes. I was seriously beginning to doubt my ability to complete a full marathon!

For the next couple of weeks, my knee and right inner ankle would begin to hurt again in any run longer than 45 minutes. I also noticed that even a slight slant to a path I was running on intensified the pain in both knee and ankle. I still had a 3:00-3:15 run to do, three weeks before the marathon. As it was I ended up missing out on two important LSD runs because of injury. In hindsight, I believe that if I had have begun training a few weeks earlier (as this programme does) and had made the runs longer more gradually, I would have been able to handle the LSD runs and the final stages of the marathon more comfortably.

At this stage I had to make some decisions about the training. For the last three weeks I decided to do only 30 to 45-minute runs again, with a rest day after every couple of sessions. The knee and ankle were really worrying me and I knew that if they didn't feel good by marathon day, then the run probably wouldn't be too smooth. The other decision was to leave out the final 3:00-3:15 LSD run altogether. I felt that if I attempted another run of that length, then three weeks might be too little recovery time if the same problems were aggravated. I wanted to concentrate on getting my knee and ankle feeling strong.

In the end the solution to my knee problem was quite simple. I explain it more fully in the chapter on 'Common Running Injuries', but all I needed to do was wear a simple band that straps around the leg just below the knee and over the patellar tendon.

I purchased such a band at a sports exposition two days before the marathon, when I went to pick up my race number. It was a gamble, because I had never run with one before. However, I thought that I didn't have much to lose and if it wasn't working then I could always take it off during the run. As it turned out, over the entire distance my knee didn't give me one second of trouble – so I was extremely happy!

Unlike the knee, my ankle was a problem as it began to ache after the first hour of the marathon. The pain was dull and luckily not bad enough to keep me from running the whole distance, but it took quite a while after the marathon before I could run properly again without feeling soreness.

Leg muscle tenderness

Due to the nature of marathon training it is normal to expect a certain degree of muscle and connective tissue **soreness** in the legs after some sessions. The muscles most affected on me were the calves, shins and also the quadriceps (front of thigh) after longer runs. This is where **massage** can be applied effectively to aid recovery.

The idea of massaging the legs after training is basically to help prevent a build up of aches and pains, and speed up the recovery process. Massage is effective for several reasons:

♦ Muscle stiffness is released because structures like the fascia (tissue surrounding and connecting muscles) can be specifically worked on.

♦ Blood circulation in the muscles, joints and connective tissues is enhanced by the pumping action of massage movements. This means that oxygen and nutrient-enriched blood (which would have been restricted in movement by tense muscles) flows more freely to the structures, ensuring quicker recovery and growth.

- The improved fluid circulation also enhances the removal of any metabolic waste products that have formed in the tissues during hard training. This helps minimise the amount of soreness felt after the session.

- The flexibility of muscles can be improved by the therapist massaging the fibres in a variety of directions. This can aid in preventing future training injuries.

- Massage can help to break down scar tissue and adhesions that have formed in muscles and connective tissues as a result of past injuries. Untreated, these can lead to tension and a lack of flexibility in the affected structures.

- A good massage leaves you feeling relaxed, flexible and keen to face the next training session!

Ideally massages should be obtained regularly to assist you with training, and especially after LSD runs when there has been extra stress. Of course, this will depend on access to a therapist, the amount they charge for a massage, and how much spare time you have. A session usually lasts anywhere from between 30 to 90 minutes.

It is not a good idea to wait until just before the marathon to experience a massage, as you need to become familiar with how your body will react to one. Sometimes a massage can leave you with a headache or nausea the following day if it has speeded up the removal of any toxins in the body. It is better to have several during the course of your marathon preparation, with a final gentle one a week or so before marathon day.

I operate my own massage therapy clinic so also do massage on myself to relieve muscle tension (it's not as relaxing as getting one from somebody else though!). I had to pay particular attention to my calf and shin muscles and would massage them regularly whilst watching television. I used either one of the oils I mix myself for clients, or an **Arnica**-based cream. Aromatherapy and massage books and courses teach how to make your own special oil mixes if you are interested in that aspect. Arnica salve is a homeopathic remedy intended for use in the case of sprains and external swelling and bruising, and it is meant to have a stimulating effect on the blood flow related to the muscles and joints rubbed. This all adds up to faster recovery times between training sessions.

If you are interested in learning about **self-massage** techniques, then you should be able to find suitable sports massage reference books from a good bookstore. You can also take a basic relaxation massage course to learn more fully what to do. Various educational institutions often teach short introductory massage courses that are worthwhile participating in. It is important to have a basic knowledge of massage techniques before you put them to use as there are correct and incorrect ways to massage. Sometimes there are also contraindications to massage (when you shouldn't massage), which include the presence of acute injury, infections, tumours, or varicose veins.

Frame of mind

This is the last complication that I wanted to address. After my not so successful final LSD run of 2:45, my mental outlook at that time was not too optimistic. Sometimes you will be faced with situations that make you doubt your ability to make it to and through marathon day. There may be times when you feel like it is not worth the trouble to keep training with the marathon completion as your goal. I experienced such feelings after setbacks like an injury, and even when I was out running in horrible weather conditions, knowing that I could have been cosy, dry and inside reading a book instead!

This is when the struggle gets interesting and the advice is simple – don't let your mind talk you unreasonably out of losing sight of your goal. Grit your teeth and **keep going**. Remember that if doing a marathon were easy then everyone would do it. Regardless of how well you run the marathon, just making it to the starting line is a big achievement. Remaining strong mentally will help you get through any physical problems too!

One of the main problems with injury and the like is that they are a setback to your finely tuned training plan. All this requires is a shift in your thinking. Don't think that there is no way out. Be prepared to **modify** the plan if necessary so that you can still retain cardiovascular fitness through other training forms such as swimming, cycling etc., whilst recovering from an injury. Stay focussed on a goal that you want badly enough, and you will usually be able to find ways around problems. If there is a major setback too close to the marathon day for you to recover from, then at least you know you gave it your best shot – and there is always next year!

Chapter Five Summary

⇨ Don't let being away from your home training area be an excuse to disrupt training.

⇨ Be aware of physical feelings when you train – is there a feeling that some body part is weak or causing you discomfort? Follow it up.

⇨ If you are prone to stitches, experiment with different factors to see what can help prevent them.

⇨ Pressing on the stitch site when it occurs can help relieve the pain.

⇨ Don't sit in front of a computer with bent legs for a long time straight after running!

⇨ Make sure a muscle tear (or any injury)is properly healed before recommencing training.

⇨ Stop early on in a LSD run to fix anything that is causing you discomfort.

⇨ New shoes can create blisters in the first few sessions they are used.

⇨ Consult a sports injury specialist when a physical problem remains.

⇨ Incorporate massage into your schedule as an aid to faster recovery.

⇨ Don't be talked unreasonably out of doing the marathon when the going gets tough – get tough back!

Chapter Six
What to Eat

"High-grade performance requires an input of high-grade fuel."

There is no question that what you eat affects the way in which you cope with daily training and so, ultimately, the marathon itself. To maintain a healthy body, ingested foods must contain the necessary nutrients in the right amounts, and must also supply enough fuel to get you through the training sessions.

A healthy diet contains adequate amounts of **carbohydrates, fats, proteins, vitamins, minerals, fibre** and **water.** If there is a deficiency in any one of these, then with time the body will not be able to function to its maximal ability. Serious diseases can be a result of inadequate dietary practices. Diet becomes even more vital when you are making extra demands on your body through rigorous training.

As it is important to have a basic understanding of how diet can affect the body, the next section describes each of the above nutrients and the role they play in health and training. I promise not to get too technical!

Carbohydrates (CHO)

Carbohydrates are important in an athlete's diet because the body prefers them over other substances as an energy source. They are chemicals made up of oxygen, carbon and hydrogen, and include foods such as **sugars** and **starches.** Some examples of foods containing sugars (known as either simple or refined CHO) include table sugar, honey, soft drinks, cordials, jams, sweet biscuits and cakes, beer, and confectionery. I'll be among the first to admit to having a stubborn sweet tooth, but one problem with eating a diet too high in sugar is that generally such foods lack vitamins, minerals and fibre, and they can also have a high-fat content.

Examples of foods containing starches (also referred to as the more healthy complex or unrefined CHO) include the wholemeal/whole grain varieties of cereals, pasta, rice and breads, and vegetables such as potatoes, corn, peas and carrots, legumes (dried beans and lentils), fruit, and milk and yoghurt. These last three do contain simple sugars, but they are also a source of various other nutrients. Wholemeal/whole grain products are generally considered superior to their white counterparts, which are more refined and so contain less nutrients.

Carbohydrates are broken down through the digestive process into a form of sugar that the body can then easily use. This sugar is called **glucose.** It is the body's major energy source and is needed, amongst other things, for all muscle contraction (including heart function), and the efficient functioning of the nervous system. After the digestive process, the glucose is absorbed into the bloodstream from the small intestine for immediate use, or is stored in the muscles and liver for later use. In its stored form it is called **glycogen** and this is reconverted to glucose when needed. If there is an excess of CHO, then after digestion it will be converted and stored as body fat.

The fuller your muscle and liver glycogen stores are going into the marathon, the better will be your chances of avoiding "hitting the wall" later in the run. Sports nutritionists generally recommend that our diet should consist mainly of CHO (at least 55%- 60%), and preferably the complex sort. As well as the extra vitamin, mineral and fibre content, complex CHO are absorbed and used more slowly than simple ones, which means a steady release of glucose into the bloodstream and energy available to the body for a longer time. Simple CHO are absorbed into the bloodstream quickly and so may not be metabolised properly. Due to the rapid absorption they can also quickly destabilise blood glucose levels.

Fats

Fats also provide the body with energy for activity. However, they are not the preferred fuel source because when compared with carbohydrates the body has to use more oxygen to convert them into energy. So in an energy-supplying role, fats are not as efficient as CHO.

A small amount of fat should be included in the diet otherwise there may be a deficiency in necessary fat-soluble vitamins (vitamins A, D, E, and K). Generally this would not be more than 25%

– 30% of the total daily kilojoules/kilocalories (4.186 kilojoules = 1 kilocalorie). Having too much fat in the diet is the more usual problem than having too little. A disproportionate amount of dietary fat can lead to heart disease and other circulatory problems. Obesity can be another consequence as an excess of fat from foods eaten will be stored in the body as fatty tissue. For women this storage site is often between the waist and thigh area, and for men it is stored around the abdominal region. Excess fatty tissue can often be seen in the form of lumpy, dimpled skin called cellulite.

Fats are either **saturated** or **unsaturated** depending on their chemistry, and the most damaging fats to the body are the saturated sort. A diet high in these will increase the amount of **cholesterol** in the body. Cholesterol is produced by the body, found naturally in the blood stream and body cells, and is useful in a number of processes. However, if a high cholesterol diet leads to an excessive amount in the body then the risk of atherosclerosis is increased. This is a disease where hard fatty deposits from the excess cholesterol line the inside of arteries, narrowing them over time and causing a reduced supply of blood to the tissues beyond. Heart attack and stroke are also associated with this condition. A doctor taking a blood sample for analysis can easily determine your cholesterol level.

Fats can lead to weight gain more readily than carbohydrate or protein intake. This is because a portion of fat contains over twice as many kilocalories as a same volume portion of carbohydrate or protein. One gram of fat yields 9 kilocalories, whereas 1g of carbohydrate or protein yields only around 4 kilocalories. The simple **basic principle of weight gain** is – if you consume more kilocalories of energy in a day than you use up in activity, the excess will be stored in the body as fat, with a resultant increase in weight. If you use up more energy than that supplied by what you have eaten, then you will lose weight. So if fats predominate in your diet, then you are taking in twice the number of kilocalories as opposed to having CHO or proteins as your main choices. On a high-fat diet you will put weight on more quickly and also be missing out on important nutrients.

It can be challenging to maintain a low-fat diet until you recognise which foods contain fat. Visible sources of fat include cream, butter, margarine, oils (including polyunsaturated types) and other cooking fats. Fats are often not immediately visible because they can be mixed in with other ingredients. High-fat items where the fat is less apparent include cheese, ice-cream and other dairy products (low-fat options are available), fatty meats, chocolate, cakes, pastry items, biscuits, deep-fried foods, snack foods like chips, and sauces such as mayonnaise.

Most saturated fats (the not so healthy fats) are only found in animal products, (i.e. full-fat dairy products and meats), so try keeping the intake of these sources at a moderate to low level and replace with the low-fat alternatives wherever possible. Removing all visible fat from meat (including the skin from chicken and turkey) before eating it also helps.

An easy way to monitor dietary fat intake to maintain a healthy level of body fat is to become familiar with the amount of fat in food items. A maximum of 25% – 30% of the daily kilocalories should come from fat, and this can be determined by a simple calculation. Many foods now have their nutrient content displayed on the packaging. Take an item from the supermarket shelf and look at those figures. Do the following calculation, keeping in mind that you won't take the item if its fat content supplies more than 30% of the total kilocalorie energy.

Example: a small container of full fat yoghurt.

Energy per 100g = 129 kcal

Fat content per 100g = 4.9g

These are the only two figures you need. Now multiply the fat by 9 (amount of energy supplied by 1g of fat), then divide that figure by the total kilocalories shown.

Therefore: 4.9 x 9 = 44.1

44.1 divided by 129 = 0.3418

Then multiply by 100 to get the percentage: 0.3419 x 100 = 34.18%

This means that 34.18% of the energy you are obtaining from that yoghurt is coming from fat. This is above the 30% level you wanted, so opt for a low-fat version instead.

It is an interesting exercise to go through the same process with foods you have in the cupboard. You might be surprised at the high percentage readings obtained from items you thought were low in fat and "healthy"! Once you have tested items over a period of time, it becomes much easier to know which foods can be eaten freely, and those you should eat sparingly.

Protein

Protein is the chemical compound that forms the structural frame of our muscle tissues, hair, skin and blood. An adequate dietary intake is necessary to ensure growth and the repair of damaged or worn-out tissues. An excess of protein in the diet will be either broken down and excreted as a compound called urea, or converted and stored as fat.

Proteins consist of **amino acids**, of which there are twenty. Eleven can be synthesised in the body but the other nine (called essential amino acids) must be obtained from what you eat. Protein can be obtained from plant and animal sources. Complete protein foods such as meat (including fish and poultry), eggs and dairy foods are animal sources and they contain all the essential amino acids. On their own, vegetable sources such as cereal products, nuts and dried beans do not have all the essential amino acids.

Vegetarian athletes need to ensure that they have the right combination of vegetable sources so that all the essential amino acids are present, otherwise proper body functioning can be disrupted. Choosing a legume, lentil, chick pea or bean dish (e.g. soybeans, baked beans, haricot beans) and combining it with a cereal dish containing wholemeal pasta or bread, brown rice, or corn, will ensure that all the essential amino acids are consumed. Alternatively, the cereal dish could be replaced by nuts such as raw almonds, walnuts, cashews and pecans, or seeds such as sesame, pumpkin or sunflower seeds.

As with CHO and fats, protein can also provide the body with energy. The amount used will depend upon how long the exercise lasts and how good the body's glycogen stores are. The better these stores are, the less likely that protein will be used to supply energy.

The recommended daily intake of protein depends on body weight and the type of training, but for endurance athletes about **1-1.2 g of protein per kg of body weight** is necessary. If your main supply of protein comes from animal sources, then choose the low-fat types to minimise the fat and cholesterol levels.

Vitamins and minerals

Vitamins are organic substances present in foods and which the body needs to function healthily. Diseases occur with vitamin deficiencies. One example is the disease called "scurvy", which results from a lack of vitamin C. The symptoms of advanced cases include severe anaemia and kidney failure. In earlier times this was a common complaint amongst sailors who spent long periods of time at sea without having fresh vitamin C-rich fruit or vegetables to eat.

Vitamins are given a letter code, such as A, B1, B2, D, E, etc. Some need to be replaced daily in the body (water-soluble vitamins), whereas vitamins A, D, E and K can be stored in the body's fat tissues (fat-soluble). Megadosing of these storable vitamins (i.e. taking supplements to well over the recommended daily amount) can result in toxic conditions. It is not advisable to megadose with any vitamin unless this is specifically prescribed by a qualified practitioner. Vitamin deficiencies are most likely to occur in people who do not have a healthy diet, including those on restrictive or fad diets.

Minerals are inorganic compounds that are essential to all bodily processes. They come in forms that include metals and salts, such as calcium, iron, magnesium, potassium, zinc etc. Minerals must be present for the efficient functioning of vitamins. A deficiency in even one mineral can disrupt the processes of the body, which over time can lead to a weakening and wearing out of the body structures.

Athletes have a high need for vitamins and minerals. One of the reasons for this relates to temperature regulation in the body. During training, overheating is prevented by heat loss through sweating. Minerals also leave the body in the sweat and need to be replaced. Another and especially important reason is to help the prevention of "free radicals". **Free radicals** are aggressive waste products formed during the burning of energy sources in the body. They can detrimentally affect body processes at the cellular level. An adequate intake of anti-oxidants such as vitamins A, C and E, beta-carotene and selenium can help to neutralise these free radicals.

A healthy diet should be able to supply the necessary vitamins and minerals, but food quality can be affected by factors such as – **chemicals** sprayed on them during the growth process; the **time delay** between when they are harvested and when bought from the store; the **processing** of foods like cereals; and **overcooking** of foods. Vitamins and minerals are also used more quickly by the body when you are stressed – through work, sickness, physical training, or just the everyday hectic pace of life. For these reasons it may become necessary to take supplements of what your body is lacking. If you suspect a deficiency, it can be difficult trying to determine just what you are deficient in, so seeking expert advice and undergoing some tests should help pinpoint the problem. I don't take supplements regularly, but do have a multivitamin occasionally to support my dietary nutrients.

The body absorbs minerals most effectively when they are taken in a liquid (colloidal) form. One of the minerals particularly important to athletes is **iron**. An iron deficiency will result in feelings of tiredness and weakness and training performances will not be so good as previously. This is the result of a decreased supply of oxygen to the body. The lowered iron level results in a drop in the amount of haemoglobin produced, which is a compound found in red blood cells. It is the haemoglobin compound that attaches to and carries the oxygen from the lungs to the body tissues. This condition is called anaemia.

Due to menstruation, women lose iron more readily than men (discussed further in Chapter 7). To avoid an iron deficiency women are recommended to have a daily iron intake of 16mg (Australian standard) whereas men need to have only 7mg. Pregnant and breastfeeding women require an even higher intake, and so may need to take an iron supplement. Iron can be obtained from many foods, including red meat, leafy green vegetables, liver, oysters, cereals, beans, nuts and wheat.

Fibre

Dietary fibre is the part of plant foods that the body is not able to break down, and so is excreted as waste after the digestive process. Fibre is found in fruit, whole grain cereals, vegetables, nuts and legumes.

A diet high in fibre prevents constipation and is beneficial in the prevention of a number of digestive tract complaints. It also aids athletes in training, as fibre ensures a slower release of sugars from food. This prevents large fluctuations in blood sugar levels (which can result from quickly absorbed sugars) and allows a more sustained release of energy.

One of my favourite daily health and fibre sources is the kiwi fruit – also called a Chinese gooseberry. Get them ripe, give them a rinse and rub in some water, then cut into pieces and enjoy – skin and all. Delicious, and guaranteed to keep you regular! I find it much easier to have a high fibre intake during summer, when I go crazy over all the wonderful tropical and stone fruits available. Now in their fifties, my parents have for some time given their health a boost by eating a huge plateful of different fruits for their midday meal. Regular exercise has become more important to them too. It's great to see people who are close to you taking a real interest in their state of health!

Water

Water is essential to life and is found in all body cells. Approximately 65% of the body's mass is comprised of water, and it is needed for a number of important body functions. These include forming the bulk of the body fluids, aiding in the digestion and transportation of compounds, and assisting in maintaining body temperature.

Water is obtained through liquids and foods ingested, and also through the metabolism of food. The four ways in which it is lost from the body are through the urine and faeces, through skin pores during perspiration, and in air that is breathed out of the lungs.

The consequences of an athlete not taking in enough water were outlined in Chapter Three when **dehydration** was described. To remain properly hydrated, water intake needs to be monitored not only during exercise, but also before and after training and competitions. Even though you may feel fine exercising without drinking much for the day, your performance can be affected by even a small degree of dehydration. With intense activity the body can lose as much as 3 litres of water per hour. It is not usual to drink that amount when exercising, so this is why the body must be well hydrated beforehand, and then supplies replenished after the activity – in addition to drinking fluids during the exercise.

As mentioned, water is the best replacement fluid, and preferably not too cold or hot, as the extremes can affect absorption rate. Quick water absorption is especially important on hot days or when the exercise is very hard. **Glucose sports drinks** are also suitable as long as they are not too strong in concentration. If too strong, absorption will be poor and it may also lead to an upset stomach.

Drink some water half an hour or so before you go out to train, and if the session will last for one hour or longer, be sure to have one or two glasses of water. For the LSD sessions take a drink with you (either strapped around the waist or just a small bottle carried) and drink small amounts of 150-200ml every 15 to 20 minutes. This will help prevent dehydration. There are individual differences between athletes so if you feel you need to drink more, then do. In my case, it is more likely that I have to keep reminding myself to drink enough!

After training it takes several hours for the body to properly re-hydrate. Liquid stores can be replenished with water, fruit juice, or tea. Teas should preferably be herbal (but not diuretic or laxative teas), as "normal" teas contain caffeine.

Eating habits

I am 164cm (5ft 4ins) and weigh about 56kg. I tend to lose a kilo or two in summer (more activity and less heavy foods) and put it back on during winter (one reason I like summer better than winter!). The heaviest I have been was 68kg, when I was into bodybuilding seriously for a year back in 1987. That was a great experience, but I prefer to stay fit at around the 56kg mark now. I mention these figures so that you can relate the amounts of foods I talk about in the next section to my size. Naturally a bigger and more active person will need to have a higher intake of calories than I do and vice versa, so read the following section with differences like that in mind. The types of food you need as an endurance athlete will be similar to what I eat, but the amounts you need may very well be more or less.

It has taken me a long time to learn to eat in a way that is healthy and good for my different sporting performances, and consequently my eating patterns have varied greatly over the years (not to mention my body shape!). The way I eat now is not necessarily the best regime for you to follow, but it will give you some idea of how another athlete approaches nutrition.

One of the most common questions asked of me by other athletes is, 'Do you follow a special diet?' I don't actually believe that "diet" is a good word to use, as we have become too used to thinking of a diet as a set eating pattern that we need to rigidly follow in order to lose weight. There are countless "fad" diets that people will spend money on, hoping to find a secret to quick weight loss. Often the result is short-term weight loss, followed not long after by an even greater weight gain, and so back to square one (or worse). To sum up this last sentence – in the long-term, **diets do not work**.

More realistically, most people gain weight from overeating and for an associated reason. If the reason is (for example) to help fight depression, then the same eating pattern that leads to weight gain will continue until the cause of the depression is determined. Once the cause is confronted and dealt with then the reason for overeating is removed and so the habit of unhealthy eating can then also be changed. I have observed over the years that when I feel happy with and about life in general and myself, I have no problems with body weight. If you are someone who constantly battles with diets and weight, it may be useful to sit back and ask yourself what the overeating and unhealthy eating patterns really stem from (and it may link to events that occurred earlier in your life). Work on your inner self, and the outer self will start working on itself!

Healthy eating habits need to be learned, and then maintained as a usual way of life. Rather than say that I follow a diet, I prefer to think of myself as maintaining a healthy way of eating. Good eating habits don't mean never having your favourite "bad" foods again, but are about knowing what makes you feel healthy and what keeps your body in shape and functioning smoothly.

It makes sense to maintain a healthy body weight as opposed to being overweight because, firstly, body organs and systems are not as likely to become diseased and, secondly, as an athlete, you don't have to carry so much bulk around when running. Don't attempt losing weight close to the marathon date as this may deplete you of valuable energy stores and leave you feeling weak. Athletes that want to lose weight are usually already exercising enough, so it is often just a matter of changing eating patterns to include high complex carbohydrate and low-fat items (and perhaps also resolving an emotional problem!). This is the sensible and effective long-term answer to healthy weight maintenance.

On a programme of healthy eating combined with adequate exercise, a realistic weight loss aim is 0.5 – 1kg per week. I have found that the best way to monitor weight loss is not by checking a set of scales daily (I don't possess any), but rather by regularly taking some body measurements, recording them and keeping a check on how well clothes fit. I take and record mid-thigh, waist and hip measurements, and check them maybe once a month.

Before and after training

On training days my usual morning routine is to get out of bed and be running within the next 45 minutes, so often I don't feel like eating that early, and especially not just before training. I will make sure that I drink something though. If I am doing a LSD run I allow extra time, so that about two hours beforehand I will eat something like wholemeal toast with a banana (complex CHO), as well as a few glasses of liquid.

Once training and the cool down stretches are over I have something to drink straight away, usually one or two glasses of water, cordial, fruit juice, herbal tea or a combination of these. Then I like to have some low-fat yoghurt and fruit.

To make sure I drink enough through the day I always have a full glass of flat mineral water on the bench. I prefer drinking bottled mineral water to chlorinated tap water, and flat compared to gaseous water. Apparently, flat water is also better than fizzy water if you have a problem with cellulite. As soon as I have a drink I just refill the glass, so I am reminded to drink whenever I see it. I drink more on some days than on others, but if I only drank when I felt thirsty I would not end up drinking much at all. I have had to teach myself to drink more. Different individuals will have different requirements, but I probably drink 750ml – 1 litre of water per day, with extra for LSD sessions and in summer. It is a good idea not to drink much during meals as this dilutes your digestive juices, reducing their efficiency.

Breakfast

A good breakfast gives the body **energy** for the morning activities ahead. I find that I function best on three reasonably sized but not huge meals, along with several healthy snacks throughout the day. Doing this keeps my energy levels up and there is also the benefit of not over-stressing the digestive system. The traditional three large meals a day (often with an entrée and/or dessert for lunch and dinner) are taxing on the digestive organs, which are trying to sort out in which order to digest and metabolise everything.

Often I don't feel like eating much until some time after morning training. There is no problem with this as long as you do have something during the morning to restock the body's glycogen stores after training. This is best achieved by eating complex CHO, and within four hours of the session. The harder the training session, the more quickly the glycogen fuel stores are used up. Using up this stored muscle glycogen is associated with feeling fatigued, so it is important to make sure a good storage level is maintained.

When I do feel ready to eat then I'll have some toast with jam or vegemite (marmite) or some untoasted muesli (the sort with fruit and nuts) with low-fat milk and a spoonful of healthy linseed oil. Other breakfast possibilities include any number of healthy cereals now available (check the contents label for untoasted, no sugar, low-fat, high fibre etc.), muffins, pancakes (not with high-fat toppings!), baked beans, and porridge. These are all good carbohydrate sources.

Mid-morning I usually get stuck into some whole grain crackers with a mild tomato salsa dip. Salsa is a great spicy tasting Mexican tomato dip with a zero fat content. If you're a good cook with spare time you can make your own, but I just buy it from the supermarket! I might also snack on a handful of nuts, seeds and dried fruit, such as almonds, sunflower seeds and naturally dried apricots.

Lunch

The proper lunch foods will give you enough energy for the afternoon's activities, and this is especially important if you train mid to late afternoon after work. Often I hear of people complaining about how tired they are throughout the day. When they tell me what their average diet consists of, part of their problem is obvious. A fairly common example would be – `for breakfast I had coffee and a piece of white toast with peanut butter (if anything at all during the rush to get ready for work!); lunch was coffee and a ham and cheese sandwich (again low fibre and high fat); and for the evening meal I had some . . .' – generally another dish high in fat and low in fibre, minerals and nutrients. It is obvious from an example like this that the person is trying to work actively through the day but is not putting much of the right fuel into the body to do it. The emphasis has been on high fat items instead of the energy-giving complex CHO.

Eating a lunch that is high in fat and sugars and low in complex CHO will cause your **blood sugar levels** to rise and fall quickly, which leads to feelings of tiredness and lethargy in the afternoon hours. This is when you often grab a snack to keep going. If the snack is something like a chocolate bar then the cycle of a short-term high followed by feeling tired again will continue. Adding a protein food to lunchtime CHO can help to keep the blood sugar levels more stable during the afternoon.

Examples of fatiguing lunch foods include fatty or deep-fried foods such as chips, doughnuts, sausages, chocolate bars, ice-cream, croissants, creamy cakes and high-fat cheese, and items high in simple sugars like soft drinks, biscuits and many other foods that can be bought from the bakery/takeaway shop/canteen. As well as making you tired and straining the digestive system, a diet based predominantly on high calorie foods like these can also easily lead to weight gain. Too much salt, caffeine (found in normal tea, coffee and chocolate), nicotine and alcohol also cause fatigue.

Lunch for me is generally between 12.30 and 2.00pm, depending on when I feel hungry. Sometimes there is a tendency to go by the clock too much with regards to when to eat, rather than by when your body tells you it really is hungry. I like variety in foods and so don't eat the same things from day to day. I eat combinations of soup, sandwiches, tuna, salmon, sardines, eggs, fruit, steamed vegetables and salad or pasta leftovers from the night before – whatever takes my fancy at the time. One of my favourites is sardine sandwiches made with really dark, grainy bread and a dollop of tomato sauce on top of the sardines. This combination tastes great but is not so good if you are into food combining (keeping carbohydrates and proteins separate from each other)!

It can seem like a hassle to make your own lunch to take to work, but this is often much healthier than buying something from a shop, and easier on the wallet too. Sandwiches are quick and easy to make and there are all sorts of fillings that can be used. Try to use good quality unrefined bread. Breads that are brown and dark brown (make sure it's not just colouring) and which contain grains and seeds will provide you with a flavoursome source of CHO, fibre and minerals. It is a good idea to check the label to avoid buying breads that are made with artificial chemicals – the more natural it is, the better it is for you. If you have an allergy to yeast, sourdough bread is one yummy bread that is yeast free, and health food stores will often have other varieties too.

Some suggestions for sandwich fillings are: grated or sliced raw vegetables; sliced banana with honey and cinnamon; curried or plain mashed boiled eggs; mashed avocado; fish such as sardines, tuna or salmon; tofu; chicken; and tahini (sesame seed paste). Herbs and spices can be used to add extra flavour. Sometimes I use leftovers from the previous evening meal, such as steamed vegetables or pasta. Many of these items can be put together into any sort of combination you fancy – experiment!

Personally, I prefer not to use margarine because of the manufacturing process it has gone through (I also avoid artificial sweeteners) and I use butter in moderation because of its high-fat content. These fats are found in many bakery items such as cakes, biscuits and pastries, and if you are trying to lose weight then reducing your intake of such items will definitely speed up the process.

Other lunch possibilities include any number of soups, salads of pasta, rice, bean or tabouleh, an omelette and wholemeal pancakes. These can be complimented with a fresh salad, a fruit smoothie or a freshly squeezed fruit or vegetable juice. Many lunch dishes can be made quickly and ahead of time to be taken to work with you. There are certainly more lunch options than those I have mentioned here, but this is just a list to help get your creative processes going!

If you have to or want to eat out at lunchtimes, take the time to choose healthy meals. Stick with fresh, low-fat natural foods that are not deep-fried or covered in creamy sauces. Many restaurants and cafés do now offer a wide range of healthy sandwich options and salad bars. Be wary of high calorie desserts and opt for fresh fruit dishes instead. You can always ask the chef if the dish can be modified to your liking (e.g. having grilled fish rather than deep-fried) – after all it's your body that the food is going into!

Snacks

As already mentioned, I like to have some snacks during the day when I get peckish. If my body is telling me that it is hungry then it is only good sense to put some fuel into it. On some days I will need more snacks than on others, depending on my activity level. Some examples of snacks that I choose from include: small quantities of nuts, seeds and dried fruits (because although healthy they are still high in calories), fresh fruit, low-fat yoghurt, whole grain crackers and salsa, freshly made plain popcorn, and wholemeal malt biscuits. I generally try to ensure that less than 30% of the item's energy comes from fat.

Sometimes during a meal or when you are thinking about a snack, your body may trick you into thinking you are hungry when you are actually not. To determine if it is real hunger, try what I call the **"saliva test"**. Think of food or another mouthful of what you are eating and if you don't salivate then your body probably doesn't need it at that time. That's one trick that works for me to avoid overeating (even if you really want to finish everything on the plate!).

Dinner

Generally I like meals that are quick to prepare. This stems from the days when I came home from work late, tired and with little time before I had to go out again. I am not a vegetarian, but do try to have at least a couple of days a week that are meat-free. Then I cook meals that use pasta, eggs, legumes, or tofu.

Some of my evening meals begin with soup (usually not the creamy sorts). The main course will be cooked in a non-stick pan or in the oven. I never deep-fry food and use only small amounts of virgin olive oil in the pan. Reasons not to eat deep-fried foods include their high-fat content and the fact that the high cooking temperatures used alters the structure of the fats. The body cannot easily break down such fats and this basically leads to a weakening of the body systems.

I prefer to make meals like stir-fry, with vegetables and meat or tofu, fish dishes, casseroles, wholemeal pasta with a tomato and vegetable sauce (from the supermarket again!), omelettes, chilli con carne – anything that's quick. Brown rice, wholemeal pasta and couscous all make tasty side dishes.

A selection of three or four lightly steamed vegetables (such as broccoli, cauliflower, carrot, zucchini, sprouts, spinach or corn), and/or a fresh salad makes a wonderful accompaniment. I find steamed vegetables much tastier than boiled ones, and they also retain more vitamins and minerals. Eating fresh salads (i.e. not a mayonnaise-loaded potato salad) gives your body lots of vitamins and minerals and helps to boost your immune system to ward off illnesses. I make salads with a dressing that consists of salad vinegar and an equal amount of olive oil, minced garlic, lemon juice, honey and mustard (experiment with the amounts to get the flavour you like), all shaken together in a bottle. There should be enough to just cover all the salad ingredients once the dressing is poured on and they are mixed together.

The salad ingredients themselves can include any combination of a couple of lettuce varieties, tomatoes, pre-packaged and chopped soup vegetables, salad onions, gherkins, olives, seeds, avocado, chopped hard-boiled eggs, chick peas, corn kernels, and some feta cheese cubes. Herbs and spices add extra flavour. If you're really concerned about losing weight, go easy on items such as the olives, avocado, feta cheese and oil in the dressing.

Sweet desserts are a nice way to end the meal if you have a sweet tooth like me, but they are also one of the best ways to get the excess calories that head straight for the fat cells after being eaten. I tend not to have desserts and don't buy them to keep in the house either. Having a carton of chocolate ice cream or ready made fruit pies in the fridge would just be too tempting! There are a few ways to get around the dessert challenge. One way is to make sure there is enough in the main meal, having soup as a starter if necessary. Another is to stick to low-fat dessert items like fresh or stewed fruit, or have some low-fat yoghurt with honey or berries stirred in.

I don't believe in **never** having calorie-dense foods, as once you tell yourself there is a food you are not allowed to eat, you're likely to develop a craving for that food which will drive you crazy! (One reason diets don't work.) So occasionally I do have a dessert. This is usually when I go out to eat, or make a chocolate pudding or apple crumble to add some life to a dull grey winter day. The nice things about having an occasional dessert like this are that you really appreciate it, and you have fewer hassles with gaining weight than you would if you ate them on a regular basis.

Sweet-tooth Saturday

To continue with the theme of the last paragraph, I also get asked how I manage to stay away from 'junk' foods. The easy answer is that I **don't** all of the time. But instead of trying to monitor how much chocolate or other sweet foods I should or shouldn't have in a week, I follow the habit of eating healthily during the week then letting myself have whatever sweet foods I want on Saturdays. This way, my body stays in shape and my mind does too!

Imagine that if the average person saved all the snack foods, chocolate bars and biscuits, ice cream and cakes they would normally eat during the week until the Saturday, they would probably find it difficult to eat all of those calories, fats and simple CHO on the one day. I find it quite a good solution to maintaining a healthy weight, and still treating my taste buds. Why drive yourself crazy with cravings when you can have the best of both worlds? I actually find that once you take on low fat eating habits, you can't handle lots of junk food on the Saturday anyway. You are more in touch with how much healthier your body is feeling, so you don't overindulge in too many sweet things. It feels nice to have some once a week though!

Preparing for the marathon

Now that you have an idea of another runner's eating habits – which of course vary with individual preferences – I will cover nutrition in the days leading up to the marathon. The marathon is the ultimate goal here, it is important to know which foods **you** need to eat on the night prior to and the morning of an LSD session (rehearsing for the marathon) to make you feel the best. By this I mean that you wake up feeling energetic and raring to go.

The following is a nutritional summary of what to eat prior to the marathon (based on a 12pm start time as for the Rotterdam marathon):

* For the **7 days prior** to the event, increase intake of complex CHO foods so that they supply about 70% of your energy intake.
* Make sure that you are keeping well hydrated with water, and fruit juice or training drinks.

The day before

* In the morning, continue eating your usual meals that are high in complex CHO and dietary fibre. Stay well hydrated.
* For the evening meal stick with what has worked best for you prior to LSD sessions. For me this was a meal of boiled brown rice, steamed vegetables and a piece of skinless chicken. You may prefer to have a rice or pasta dish without the meat. Make sure the meal is low in fat, so no creamy sauces, and **don't over-eat.**

Marathon day

Nerves may prevent you from feeling too hungry, but you still need to have a final meal of some sort to make sure your energy stores are well stocked.

* Have your pre-event meal at least **2 – 3 hours before** the start to allow the stomach to empty and blood sugar levels to stabilise.
* Use **easy to digest foods** that are **low in fat and fibre**. This is because fats will slow the digestion process, and eating too much fibre at this stage will increase the need for you to have a bowel movement (not handy during the race!).

My pre-run breakfast choice was wholemeal toast with chopped bananas, but use whatever has worked well for you in training. Once again, don't overeat.

- If you find it difficult to eat solids for this meal, have a low fat, high carbohydrate liquid meal that you have tried and liked in training.
- From 2 hours and less to the start, have only water or dilute sports drink. Have one or two glasses 30 minutes before the start.

During the marathon

- Drink at every drink station (or every 15-20 minutes) — as much as you would have during a LSD session, and the same type of fluids.
- There will also often be **sponge stations**, so that you can squeeze water over your head in warmer conditions. This is very refreshing when you are tired and hot. Used sponges and drink containers usually just get thrown onto the road when the runners are finished with them.
- If you **ate** something during LSD training sessions then have the same food with you for during the marathon.
- **Glucose tablets** can come in handy during the tougher final stages.

After the marathon

- **Drink**, drink, drink to replace all the liquid you have lost over the last few hours. It can take the best part of a day for your body to become properly re-hydrated after a hard run.
- The best way to replenish your depleted energy stores is to **eat** the same as you used to fill them up. **Complex CHO** eaten within **2 to 4 hours** after the marathon will ensure a good start to the replenishment of glycogen stores. Give the body a chance to settle down immediately after the run, so don't go eating a huge amount of food straight away.

There were banana and orange pieces supplied at the finish of the Rotterdam marathon, and I can remember thinking it was the nicest food I'd eaten in a long time! When I found Mart I also got stuck into a sandwich I had packed earlier that morning to take along.

- In the days straight after the marathon, keep drinking plenty and stick with the high CHO diet. I also had a few treats of the more simple CHO variety during the recovery phase to help celebrate my achievement!

Chapter Six Summary

⇨ Sporting performances will not be optimal if you have poor eating habits.

⇨ Ensure that your regular training diet is at least 60% complex CHO.

⇨ Fats in the diet are necessary, but should be unsaturated and provide no more than 30% of the total daily kilocalories. Choose low-fat food items.

⇨ A recommended daily intake of protein is 1-1.2g/kg of body weight.

⇨ A supplement may be necessary if your meals do not provide all the vitamins and minerals your body needs.

⇨ A deficiency in iron will lead to feelings of fatigue and weakness.

⇨ The best foods to eat are unprocessed and as close to natural as possible.

⇨ Dietary fibre helps protect the digestive system and ensures a slower release of sugars from food, giving a more sustained release of energy.

⇨ Proper hydration is necessary to prevent dehydration during exercise.

⇨ Restock energy stores by eating complex CHO 2 to 4 hours after exercise stops.

⇨ Healthy eating habits that are a way of life are best.

⇨ Diets don't work in the long term.

⇨ Don't attempt to lose weight close to the marathon.

⇨ Eat when you are hungry, and mainly energy-giving complex CHO where possible.

⇨ If you are hungry between main meals, have low-fat, high fibre snacks.

⇨ If you are feeling "burnt out" in the afternoons, check your eating and sleeping patterns.

⇨ If you have a problem with weight, don't have calorie-dense foods in the house.

⇨ Try allowing yourself some not so healthy foods one day a week.

⇨ Work on your inner self, and the outer self will start working on itself!

⇨ Know which foods and drinks will work best for you on marathon day by rehearsing with them during the LSD sessions.

Chapter Seven

Especially for Women

'When you have the desire to achieve, there are no limits.'

This chapter covers points that are generally specific to females, but male readers will also be able to make use of the information in some of the sections.

Marathons for women

It might surprise you to know that women have not always been allowed to compete in the marathon race. Women's marathons were not made legal until 1972, but in 1967 the first woman to run one officially was an American named Katherine Switzer. She entered the Boston marathon as K.V. Switzer. To enable her to finish, her boyfriend had to contend with the race co-director who was trying to throw her off the course. As a result of the run, Katherine was suspended from the Amateur Athletic Union. At that time the furthest a woman was permitted to run was 2.5km!

In 1971 Australian runner Adrienne Beams was the first woman to run less than 3 hours in a marathon, and still there was no Olympic marathon event for women. There were common beliefs that endurance running would cause infertility and other physical problems in women; women just could not cope with long-distance running, and women who ran such distances would lose their femininity! The International Olympic Committee decided to put forward a requirement that there had to be women from 25 countries and 2 continents regularly running the full marathon distance before it would consider a women's Olympic marathon. This requirement was met in 1979 when the American cosmetics company Avon organised a race in Waldniel, West Germany. The start list consisted of more than 250 women, from 5 continents and 25 countries. A marathon for women had also been held in 1978 in the USA. Women were already running impressive times over the marathon distance, as indicated by the 1980 Avon Championship in London, where 10 of the competitors ran faster than 2:40. Women were finally permitted to run the marathon for the first time as an Olympic event in 1984 in Los Angeles – and we've come a long way since then!

Menstruation and the athlete

Having a monthly period affects different women in different ways. It is generally acknowledged that menstruation does not affect athletic performance. Women participate successfully in competitions at all levels and at all times of their cycles. Speaking for myself, I seem to feel physically at my best around when my period is ending. It is then that I feel more energetic and with excess body fluid gone, lighter again. Some of my best performances – including the Rotterdam marathon – have been at this time of my cycle. It is handy to keep track of your performances in relation to what time of the month it is, to come to your own conclusions about when you are feeling the best physically.

Pre-menstrual syndrome (PMS)

Pre-menstrual syndrome is a condition that affects many women, most noticeably in the week or so leading up to when a period begins. Some women have little trouble with their cycles, but others can experience a wide variety of activity-hindering symptoms. When you are in touch with the way your body works and feels, then problems such as period pain and other PMS symptoms can be alleviated or even eliminated. They should never have to be a reason for you not training or competing.

PMS is caused by fluctuating hormone levels and can include the experiencing of a number of different symptoms. The main types of symptoms include anxiety, depression, swelling (such as abdominal bloating, swollen breasts, fingers and ankles), and an increase in appetite (especially cravings for sweet foods). An individual may experience very few, some or all of the symptoms listed, and may be affected only mildly or to a state nearing incapacitation. When running, your legs may feel heavier and you may experience a general feeling of lethargy, so it can be more difficult than usual to motivate yourself to go out and train. You may notice a slight gain in weight at this time due to fluid retention, or have headaches, or generally feel irritable and argumentative. I forewarn my partner a couple of days before my period starts, because I know that I am much more likely to be snappier and be looking for arguments – and if you're both on the lookout for it, it's easier to understand what's happening!

The role that hormones play in PMS can be tricky to follow, but here is a simplified version of what happens each month.

* The pituitary gland (situated at the base of the brain) produces a hormone that causes an ovarian egg to ripen, and the ovaries to produce the sex hormone oestrogen.

* The oestrogen produced during the 2-week ripening time causes the lining of the uterus to thicken in preparation for the implantation of a fertilised egg.

* A second sex hormone -progesterone- is then produced and ovulation will occur (release of a mature egg).

* A hormonal message is received to confirm whether or not the egg has been fertilised on its way to the uterus.

* During the second 2 weeks, if there is no conception the oestrogen and progesterone levels fall and the lining of the uterus is shed in menstruation.

* This lowering of oestrogen and progesterone occurs in the week or so before menstruation, and it is this fluctuation which causes PMS.

* At the start of a period, levels of oestrogen and progesterone are at their lowest. By the end of the period, oestrogen levels have started to rise again.

If you take the oestrogen-progesterone combination contraceptive pill, there is no ovulation (usually) because there is no hormonal fluctuation, and consequently no fertilised egg. However, in the fourth week of the cycle, when you stop taking the pill, the hormone levels decrease and pre-menstrual symptoms can be experienced before your period begins.

If in tune with your body, it is easier to recognise the different stages. I have found that the best way to minimise my symptoms is to get out and train. It is when I least feel like training, but when I really benefit from the exercise, even if I make it slower and easier training than usual. I find it clears my head, relaxes me and keeps my body systems functioning smoothly. I also want to eat more sweet foods, so I give in to some cravings (on

Saturdays) but try not to go overboard with the chocolate! Sweet cravings during the week can be dampened with a spoonful of honey. It is also a good time to drink extra water and herbal teas, but a time to go easy on the salty foods as these will encourage further fluid retention. If you suffer from headaches, drink herbal peppermint tea and massage your temples with a lavender massage oil mix. Doing yoga is a gentle and beneficial method of exercising that can also help diminish PMS symptoms.

If you are affected severely by PMS then you should seek some form of help, **don't just put up with it.** Relief may be obtained with conventionally prescribed medicines, or alternatively there are some very effective tested natural remedies available through homeopaths and from many health stores. If you suffer from PMS, it could be worth your while going to the local health store and asking a qualified advisor what natural remedies they have. It may be as simple as taking a specific vitamin or mineral supplement, such as a vitamin B complex or magnesium. A good herbalist should also be able to offer an effective remedy based on your individual symptoms, and acupuncture treatments may also provide some relief.

There are certain foods that may aggravate PMS symptoms. These include caffeine drinks such as coffee, cola and normal tea, chocolate (I still end up eating some though!) and other sugary foods. Also implicated are beef and pork products, biscuits and other refined foods, cakes and products containing hydrogenated vegetable fats, artificial sweeteners, and salty foods (watch out for foods containing the salty artificial flavour enhancer called monosodium glutamate – E621). Foods that can help **diminish** symptoms include fresh fruits, vegetables and salads, nuts, brown rice, fish oils, cheese, yoghurt, lots of fresh water and relaxing herbal teas such as chamomile or peppermint. Extra work or family related stresses at pre-menstruation time also tend to aggravate the situation, so it is a good idea to make some quiet time for yourself by going for a walk, relaxing in a bath or treating yourself to a massage. Having a half-hour or so just to yourself each day does not mean that the world will stop turning!

Amenorrhoea (lack or loss of periods) and Osteoporosis

Females generally experience their first period from as early as the age of 8 to as late as 16 or so. Although heredity is an important factor, I believe that it was the large amount of time I devoted to sports (especially running, swimming and Nordic skiing) which delayed my menstrual maturity to the age of 16. I was slim due to sport and there is possibly a direct link between the amount of body fat and the presence or absence of a period. Menstruation occurs once the maturation hormones signal that the body is capable of supporting a life (pregnancy). If the percentage of body fat drops below that perceived as necessary to support a life, then there is no reason for the reproductive system to continue releasing eggs until the "famine" is over and a more suitable body fat percentage is reached again. This means that the monthly period will also cease until that time. This condition is called amenorrhoea.

Female athletes (particularly young ones) can create this condition by losing most of their body fat through hard training. This occurred to me in my early twenties, before I had more sense about training and healthy eating habits. I was training two or three times each day and surviving on yoghurt and steamed vegetables (and not much of either). Luckily, I soon went away with a ski team and got back into a healthy training and eating pattern with them. My periods did stop for a couple of months but then resumed again to the day once I had gained 3 or so kilograms (which also took the percentage of body fat above the perceived "famine" level).

It is natural, of course, for your periods to stop when you are pregnant, breastfeeding, or have reached the menopause. If you do experience amenorrhoea it is wise to consult a doctor to determine if it is training that has caused the condition. Other possibilities for the cessation of periods include the taking of certain drugs, stressful lifestyle changes, hormonal disturbances, or problems with the ovaries (such as growths).

One of the problems associated with amenorrhea is that the levels of oestrogen are lowered. This can increase the risk of bone density loss and the development of osteoporosis later in life (particularly after menopause). Osteoporosis is a condition where the bones lose some of their density and become brittle, meaning that they can fracture or break more easily. To help lower the risk of this occurring – don't smoke, have a zero to low alcohol intake, and ensure you are getting enough calcium (the average daily requirement is 800mg). Dairy products are a good source of natural calcium. A regular healthy exposure to sunlight (minimum of a half-hour per day) helps by manufacturing vitamin D in the body. Vitamin D aids the bones in absorbing calcium. Weight-bearing physical activity such as running, walking or weight training also helps prevent osteoporosis by strengthening the bones.

Anaemia

In the previous chapter I mentioned that **iron** was a mineral of particular importance to athletes and that a deficiency of it would result in the condition called anaemia. Anaemia means an insufficient level of haemoglobin in the blood. Even though iron is found in many food sources (including red meat, leafy green vegetables, liver, oysters, cereals, beans, nuts, wheat), strenuous training coupled with a poor diet or a lifestyle that is over-stressful in other areas will use up vitamin and mineral stores more quickly than usual. Iron is also lost more rapidly during menstruation, so pay special attention to diet at that time of the month.

If you are feeling tired and weak, and your training performances don't feel as good as they should, then you could suspect an iron deficiency (make sure it's not just a case of over-training). The run-down and weak feelings come from the decreased amount of oxygen molecules being transported to your body cells. The transporting compound is called haemoglobin (Hb) and iron is needed to make it. If the iron level is low then the amount of Hb in the bloodstream will also be low, hence the insufficient oxygen supplies.

One way to determine if you have anaemia caused by iron deficiency is to have a blood test done for Hb and iron levels. If a doctor diagnoses a simple case of iron deficiency anaemia (caused by diet deficiency or menstruation), iron supplement tablets along with improved dietary practices should properly restore the iron levels so that this is no longer a factor in fatigue.

Pregnancy and training

During the first month of pregnancy most women experience fatigue. It can be beneficial to rest more often but at the same time to also continue with regular exercise. Heart rate is higher during pregnancy (by 10 to 15 beats per minute) due to the increased blood flow to organs. Extra stress is experienced by the body because of this and the increasing body weight. By the end of the pregnancy, the tissues in the pelvic region (especially in the pelvic floor) have weakened. This is a physiological mechanism to ensure that the baby can pass along the birth canal. Other joints and connective tissues throughout the body may also have weakened. This occurs due to the hormone production of oestrogen and, in particular, progesterone by the placenta.

With the combination of increased weight and weakened joints, the wrong types of exercise (i.e. movements that over-stress the joints, particularly those in the lower body) can lead to injuries. After delivery it takes about three to four months before the connective tissues revert to their pre-pregnancy state and strength.

This is one area where I can't speak from first-hand experience, as I've never been pregnant. However, that doesn't stop me from having my opinions on the subject. I have athletic friends who have continued with sports like swimming and cross-country skiing well into their pregnancies and even right up to delivery day. Generally, those women did not seem to have many if any problems with the deliveries and they often resumed exercising as soon as possible after the birth as well. There are many examples of such female athletes, and some of their best sporting performances happened soon after they had a child.

I know for a fact that if I did happen to be pregnant then I would want to be exercising just as often as I do now and for as long as was comfortable. This would include running, swimming (especially in the later months), cycling, light weight training, walking and hang-gliding – until lying down became too uncomfortable! One important point though is that I am familiar with all of these exercises. Pregnancy would generally not be a good time for beginning a form of exercise you are not familiar with.

You should discuss your exercise plans with your physician, but if that is a person who rejects all forms of exercise during pregnancy I would be looking for another opinion from someone who understands where athletes are coming from. The exception of course is if you have some obstetric condition that really does limit what exercise you can do. But do find out which exercises you can and cannot do, and what the latest findings are on how exercise affects the foetus.

The basic tips for exercising when pregnant are:

- firstly, discuss with your physician the type and amount of exercise you want to do

- be prepared to have less intense training sessions after the first four months or so of pregnancy, even if you are used to hard sessions (also depends on the individual)

- if you are healthy and having a normal pregnancy, do the type of exercise you are already familiar with and enjoy doing

- be flexible, so that if it is becoming uncomfortable to continue exercising in a particular way, you modify what you are doing – e.g. if you become too large to run comfortably, consider swimming or walking instead

- find out if you need to be taking extra supplements of particular vitamins or minerals as a training and pregnant woman

- buy extra supportive and expandable training clothes!

- keep in mind that close to and for some months after the birth, care with exercise should be taken because of the weakened joints and connective tissues

Menopause

At some stage the ovaries will no longer release any eggs and will atrophy (shrink). The monthly periods stop and no more oestrogen or progesterone is produced. This is known as the menopause and usually occurs during the forties to mid-fifties (however it can occur earlier – especially if you smoke – or later). It is a process that can take several years from start to finish, beginning with **pre-menopause.** During this phase, the ovaries produce less sex hormones but in irregular quantities, which in turn causes an increase in pituitary gland hormones. These hormonal disturbances usually lead to a number of unpleasant menopausal symptoms being experienced, with the degree of severity depending on the individual. If a woman who uses the contraceptive pill continues to use it during this phase of life, many of the symptoms may actually be masked, making it more difficult to later determine whether or not menopause has actually occurred.

Pre-menopausal symptoms can include bloating, headaches, irregular periods (often longer intervals between them), abdominal cramps, depression (crying for no particular reason), sudden mild to severe mood swings, forgetfulness, insomnia (difficulty getting to sleep), a feeling that your skin is "crawling" (formication), and tingling sensations like "pins and needles". In addition, sudden surges of hormones can also create **hot flushes/flashes** – a sudden blushing feeling of being overheated. Some women experience many such flashes in a day.

Most of these symptoms can be relieved to some extent, and professional advice on the appropriate treatment should be sought by each individual. Treatment generally involves the use of hormone tablets to balance out hormone levels. Recent studies into natural hormones derived from certain plants (such as red clover) may also be worth looking at as an alternative.

As with PMS, try not to let the menopausal phase in life prevent you from continuing to enjoy exercise, competitions and life in general. Regular exercise before and during menopause is vital to help relieve the accompanying symptoms, and it is also important after menopause to help prevent osteoporosis.

Bras

Breast size is a very individual factor. As far as comfortable running is concerned, the smaller the better, but women with larger breasts don't have to sit out. A sports bra that provides adequate support is necessary. There is a common belief that running without a bra will damage the breast tissue and make them sag. But this is debatable and a sports bra is probably needed more for comfort. The breasts consist mainly of fatty tissue with milk glands and connective tissue. Due to their fat content, size can alter when you gain or lose weight. Because of the absence of muscle no exercises will increase their size or improve their tone. The breasts are attached to muscles on the chest, and if these muscles are toned then the chest may appear fuller. One such muscle toning exercise is to put the palms of your hands together in front of you at shoulder height and then push them together!

There are a variety of **sports bras** on the market now and they have a number of special features. The shoulder straps are generally wider than on normal bras and some models have cross-over straps at the back. Part of the bra may consist of perforated fabric to allow for an easier airflow. Check that the method of fastening will not dig into you during exercise, and bras with external or no cup seams will minimise chafing. Make sure to invest in a new bra well before the old one has ceased to be effective as a support, and make adjustments to the shoulder straps as the bra becomes more worn in. Good support is especially important if you get swollen and/or tender breasts leading up to menstruation, when the bouncing from running can be uncomfortable.

Make-up

I'm not into make-up as much now as when I was a teenager. Back then it was very important to me that I looked good as I was racing around the ski tracks. It was an integral part of my race preparation to make sure that the black eye liner was applied just right and for any errant skin blemishes to be well hidden under concealer! Now I prefer to be a make-up minimalist, but horses for courses, and there are some items that will help protect your skin from the elements.

Skin types differ with individuals. You may have a normal, dry or oily skin type, extremes of oily or dry, or a combination of the two. Changes in weather and how much your skin is exposed to the elements will also affect skin type. As skin ages it loses some of its elasticity and this is worsened with exposure to extreme changes in temperature. For example, if like me you are out in the strong Australian sunshine and heat one week then skiing in freezing European conditions the next, the skin tends to take a beating! Cosmetics can be used to protect your skin, but knowing which ones to use for your skin type and how much money to spend on them is the main problem. This is something to experiment with until you find a range of products you are satisfied with. Good products don't always have to cost a lot either. Get some advice from a beauty consultant about your skin type if you don't already know what it is, and you may also like to see what natural cosmetic products are available from health stores.

Sometimes we tend to use the same products all the time, when it may be better to swap brands every now and then. Otherwise the skin can get too used to what is being used on it and the cosmetics may not be as effective anymore. One of the important products is a good skin **moisturiser**. If you are outdoors a lot, then consider using a moisturiser that contains a sunscreen factor to help protect the skin. Generally the lighter your hair, the stronger the protection you need. Don't forget the neck region or the back of the hands. There are also foundations and lipsticks that contain sunscreens (baseball caps are also good face protectors during summer).

Whichever make-up you wear when training or competing, less is generally better. If you sweat at all during activity, most of it is likely to end up on your sweatband, besides which you are making it difficult for the skin to breathe if there is too much junk on top of it. I can't recall an athlete performing well because of the type of make-up they wore! If you like to wear mascara, then try the waterproof type – otherwise sweat, tears or rain could leave you looking like a racoon! Be cautious about wearing perfume in the outdoors, as some sorts can react with the sunlight and create skin disorders.

To wax or not to wax – many women like to have hairless legs. I am one of them, however I can't be bothered with the time and hassle of shaving/waxing my legs. My solution to that is simply to bleach the hairs about twice each summer so that they are not prominent. It takes only about 15 minutes a time with a hair bleach from the chemist shop and then hey presto – the dark hairs seem to have vanished. Just recently I discovered that there was a special name for someone who doesn't de-hair her legs. When I told my hairdresser about my bleaching habits she said, 'Oh, you're an Earth Chicken too!'

Eating disorders

I felt it worthwhile to include a short section on a couple of eating disorders, as they mainly affect women and often women athletes in particular. Those disorders are **anorexia nervosa** and **bulimia**. They are at opposite ends of the scale in one respect, but both can have devastating physical and psychological consequences if not checked in somebody suffering from them. A person can experience both disorders at the same time.

A person is classified as **bulimic** when they go into an eating frenzy for minutes, hours or longer and then straight away try to lose that food weight by for example, purging or vomiting it back up. A bulimic has a fear of being obese. Outwardly the person may appear to be leading a normal life and be of a reasonably normal weight. Complications can include menstrual and bowel irregularities, and fatigue. The constant purging can lead to chemical imbalances in the body, dehydration and the regurgitated stomach acid brought up can affect the throat and teeth enamel.

Anorexia is a disorder where there is an obsessive desire to lose weight by restricting food intake. An anorexic is obsessed with being thin. A distorted body image leads to the continuous belief of being fat and overweight, even when underweight. It is a difficult disease to treat, often a sufferer will not accept that there is a problem at all. In my teaching days I recall a young foreign exchange student that would come to the staff room door each lunchtime. Her appearance was very thin, pale and gaunt. She would request a cup of boiled water, and that was the extent of her lunch. This did not seem at all out of the ordinary to her.

You may be anorexic if you recognise several of the following as your own habits, and should consider seeking professional advice:

* you have an obsessive desire to be thin

* you are constantly looking in a mirror (especially without clothes to check how much fat you can see)

* you use scales daily or more frequently to check your weight

* you never think you are at a good weight and feel constantly stressed and depressed about it

* you have obsessive eating habits, such as counting calories in every mouthful, restricting meals (which are more like snacks) to

a few no fat items, or suddenly bingeing on foods which you have denied yourself

◆ you feel very fatigued

◆ you exercise excessively to burn off the food you have eaten for the day (often several exercise sessions each day)

◆ your periods have suddenly ceased.

◆ vitamin and mineral deficiencies are causing physical problems – e.g. hair loss.

◆ when eating with other people you eat normally but vomit the meal up afterwards.

◆ you regularly use laxatives in order to get the food out of your system as quickly as possible.

Advanced anorexia can lead to death because the nutritional deficiencies and other strains placed on the body ultimately cause the vital organs and body systems to shut down.

Anorexia is a disorder familiar to me because I've been there – but luckily only in the beginning stages. For a few months, all the symptoms listed above were part of my daily teenage routine, apart from the vomiting. I can't stand being physically sick at the best of times, let alone forcing myself to do it. I was training hard to be the best cross-country skier I could be, and society and coaches made it pretty clear that being thin equalled the path to success. It was in hindsight that I realised I had been well on the way to anorexia – the mirror was my television, and at a trim 54kg I was still telling myself I wasn't thin yet. During this stage I was existing on a little yoghurt and a few steamed vegetables. The laxatives were there too just in case that food was hanging around inside me too long, letting too many calories be absorbed. My periods stopped. When I went to Norway with a junior ski team, everyone complimented me on how lean I was looking, which fuelled the motivation to look even leaner! I think being with the team was what eventually snapped me out of it. We were training hard, racing, trying out new foods and I just began to eat more normally again. Seeing my teammates around me eating healthily may have been a trigger.

Having a **healthy body image** is really important. Now I realise that I can have the body shape and weight that feels good for me (55kg-57kg) as long as I eat and exercise healthily, not obsessively. Exercise has always been a way of life for me, and when I combined this with healthier eating (limiting junk food) I found it much easier to maintain the body shape I wanted. It really took me a long time to understand the links between food, mind and body, but it comes down to knowing which body shape and weight is best for you to make you feel healthy and good about yourself. When do you feel fittest? Don't strive to be of supermodel proportions, thinking that only then will you be fit and happy. Be realistic for you.

One way to calculate what a healthy weight is for your height is to use the Body Mass Index (BMI). This gives the weight range needed for you to ensure proper body functioning. A figure outside this range increases the risk of health problems occurring. The formula is: **weight (kg) divided by height (m) squared.**

So my BMI is 57 divided by (1.64) squared = 21.2

Normal BMI Ranges

Age	BMI (kg/m squared)
19-24	19-24
25-34	20-25
35-44	21-26
45-54	22-27
55-64	23-28
65+	24-29

Therefore the normal range for my age group is 20-25. Lower than 20 is considered underweight, and over 25 is overweight. As long as your weight falls within this index you can determine by how you feel which weight is best for you. Note that people with a large amount of muscle mass (muscle weighs more than fat) may score at the higher end of their range.

De-stressing

One of the main reasons why I get so many stressed-out female clients for massages is that they never spend any of the day devoted to their own health – apart from the hour they spend with me every so often. Of course men get stressed out too, but it seems more common that it is the woman who is looking after children, holding down a part or full-time job, and covering all the tasks that go along with being the house manager!

Everyone should be able to find a half-hour each day to restore his or her own sanity. **Exercise** is one way to get rid of stresses that have built up over the day but it should be enjoyable, otherwise it is just another stress creator. If you feel that training is getting tedious, take a break. Do some other type of exercise to break the routine – some tennis or swimming for example. Other de-stress options include:

* taking a slow walk so that you can take in the surroundings and give your mind a break – this can be done at any time of the day and in all sorts of weather.

* having regular "deep breathing" breaks – get plenty of oxygen to the brain and the rest of your body by inhaling as deeply as you can and holding for a count of five.

* take up yoga, which is a series of stretching and breathing exercises designed to keep the body's energy pathways open. The basic exercises can easily be learnt from an instruction book, and then practised regularly for well-being. The very easy-to-follow book from which I taught myself yoga was *Yoga: 28-Day Exercise Plan* by Richard L. Hittleman. The most recent edition ('83) was published by Bantam Books. The ISBN number you give to order or borrow a copy is 0553277480.

* sit in a quiet area for 10 minutes (longer if possible) and listen to relaxation music or just enjoy hearing nothing at all.

* if you are always busy with children at home, consider using a day care facility for a number of hours each week to give you time to yourself.

* book a regular massage.

* put on some of your favourite music and pretend you're a famous rock star by singing along loudly to it (any number of household items will do as a microphone, and don't feel self-conscious!).

* take up a relaxing hobby that you haven't done for a long time but enjoyed doing in the past – e.g. painting, colouring in, reading, playing an instrument etc.

Chapter Seven Summary

⇨ The monthly menstrual cycle can affect how you feel physically and psychologically.

⇨ PMS symptoms are caused by fluctuating hormone levels and are often noticed in the few days leading up to a period.

⇨ Physical exercise, a healthy diet and relaxation activities can all lessen PMS symptoms.

⇨ Menopause is the stage of life when the ovaries stop their functions and menstruation ceases. Hormonal treatment can help with the accompanying symptoms.

⇨ Over-training in conjunction with an inadequate diet can lead to a sudden cessation of menstruation (amenorrhoea). This can also lead to thinning of the bones.

⇨ Excessive fatigue can be due to low blood levels of Hb caused by an iron deficiency (anaemia).

⇨ Exercising during pregnancy is usually possible. Consult with your physician if you are unsure.

⇨ Sports bras are intended to provide more support for comfort during activity than normal bras do.

⇨ Consider which make-up is best for your skin care.

⇨ Be alert for signs of eating disorder habits – do any/many of the symptoms relate to you?

⇨ The Body Mass Index can be used to determine healthy body weight.

⇨ **Take the time to care for yourself, only then can you care for others as well.**

Chapter Eight

Common Running Injuries

"Difficult times help to make us stronger!"

The period of time when you are laid up with an injury can definitely be categorised as a time of difficulty and frustration for an
athlete – especially if there is a competition on the near horizon!
It doesn't matter how elite an athlete is, if a number of unfavour-
able factors arise around the same time then an injury will occur.

Prevention of an injury is always better than having to cure
one, so the key is knowing how to train and what to use so that
injuries don't occur in the first place. In Chapter 5 I described
some of the complications I experienced during training, and
this chapter outlines some more injuries that are common to
runners and how to treat them. Once you are familiar with these
descriptions then you have a better chance of knowing if you are
getting close to injuring yourself, based on symptoms that you
experience.

General definitions and R.I.C.E

It can be tempting to ignore niggling pains that appear now and
then in various body parts, especially if you adhere to the dan-
gerous adage of "pain equals gain" (where it is more probable
that pain is a sign of damage somewhere in the body). But it is
likely that a sustained feeling of pain which is more than mildly
uncomfortable is an indication that you are on the brink of sustaining an injury that will interrupt training until you heal. Even if
the discomfort is minor to begin with, the problem will not usually disappear until the cause is removed. Over time, an **acute**
injury (occurs suddenly and with intense symptoms) can become **chronic** (long lasting).

In addition to muscle and joint injuries, runners can experience strains and sprains to **tendons** and **ligaments.** A tendon
consists of bundles of tough collagen fibres that attach muscle to
bone, and a **strain** injury is used in reference to tendons and
muscles. Ligaments consist of tough connective tissue, and they

connect bone to bone. Inelastic but flexible, they limit the movement of joints. Injuries to ligaments are called **sprains**.

The treatment for most acute soft tissue injuries usually involves **R.I.C.E.** This stands for **rest, ice, compression** and **elevation.** It is a set sequence that is carried out immediately the injury has occurred.

◆ Rest – stop using the injured part as continued activity can increase the bleeding, inflammation and swelling, and may damage the tissues further.

◆ Ice – an ice pack/ice cubes wrapped in a towel and applied directly to the site (only) is used to chill the local area. Cold chills pain receptors and so decreases pain; it stops the inflammatory process, stops bleeding by slowing blood circulation, and also helps to relieve muscle spasm. With superficial or extremity injuries, cold is applied for 10 minutes at a time. For deep injuries this can be extended to 20 minutes. Once the part has warmed up again, the icing process can be repeated, and can be continued effectively for 48 hours after the injury has occurred.

◆ Compression – this is used to stop bleeding and minimise swelling. Using a hard pad over the injury site, concentrate the pressure by wrapping a bandage around it. This can be the first stage of treatment if ice is not readily available.

◆ Elevation – the injured body part needs to be kept elevated to reduce the effect of gravity. Otherwise the pressure will lead to swelling at the injury site.

Administered effectively when the injury occurs, R.I.C.E will quicken the start of the healing process and lessen the likelihood of scar tissue formation. Scar tissue is a fibrous tissue re-growth that can form in muscles, tendons or ligaments after an injury. It is inelastic tissue that restricts movement and so decreases flexibility. Deep massage at the appropriate stage is one way to limit scar tissue formation, and enhance the growth of more elastic tissues.

Depending on the severity of the injury, it is desirable to begin some form of activity relatively soon after it has occurred. This is to prevent the wasting away of muscles and other tissues. Rest alone is not always the best solution.

Rehabilitation can generally begin two to three days after the injury (when bleeding/swelling risk has decreased), and a physiotherapist may use gentle massage, heat treatments, passive exercises and ultrasound.

After seven days, fibrous tissue will be forming, so deep massage techniques can be used on mild strains, in conjunction with more active exercises. With severe strains, it is important to have accurate medical advice on what types of treatment and exercises to have and when.

The following section outlines some common runner injuries, beginning from the feet and working upwards.

Foot and ankle injuries

The feet are prone to a variety of overuse conditions, simply because of the body weight they have to support. Distance running greatly increases the forces they are subjected to.

Plantar fasciitis

The symptoms of this condition include feeling pain and soreness on the bottom of the foot under the heel, and the pain will also radiate into the midsection of the sole. The pain is worse when you get out of bed in the morning and when you first begin a training run. The pain diminishes once the foot tissues warm up, but can return again later on. The **plantar fascia** is a muscle that supports the arch of the foot. It runs down the midline of the sole from the ball of the foot to an attachment point on the heel bone (the **calcaneus**), and the tough fascia makes it non-stretchy. When the arch is not adequately supported, each running step stresses the plantar fascia and there is a pulling on it at the heel. With time there is a gradual pulling of the fascia away from the bone, and this leads to inflammation and pain. **Heel spurs** can also be a result of this problem. These are areas of new bone growth from the heel, formed in an attempt to reattach the fascia. Runners with flat or high-arched feet, and those who pronate (soles turn outwards) are most likely to experience plantar fasciitis. Other causes include wearing inflexible shoes or those with uneven heel wear, over training, or doing too much hill or speed work.

Treatment involves treating the existing inflammation and determining whether foot structure, choice of shoes or training methods are causing the problem. Anti-inflammatory substances can be used and icing the painful area after training will also help. Orthotics may be needed to provide the proper foot arch support. As a wearer of orthotics myself, it doesn't take long after a day of walking around in flat boots without orthotics to realise how much my arches have missed their usual support!

Sprained ankle

This refers to when you suddenly twist your ankle in a tripping or stumbling type accident and sprain the ligaments around the joint. Most sprains occur with trauma to the outer ankle ligaments, where the sole of the foot has rotated inwards. To stabilise the ankle joint there is one ligament on the inner ankle and three on the outer side. There are degrees of injury severity, relative to how badly the ligaments are damaged. With mild tearing of the ligaments (1st degree), there is little swelling and no joint instability. Recovery time will usually range between a few days to a few weeks. A second-degree injury involves one or two partially torn ligaments, swelling and bruising, and usually needs three to six weeks before full activity can be resumed. A third-degree injury involves the rupture (complete break) of two or more ligaments, swelling and bruising, possibly a bone fracture, and pain also on the opposite side of the sprain. Full ligament healing can take eight to twelve months.

As a guideline, if you sprain an ankle and can't walk without pain after two minutes or so, it is more than a minor injury. Immediate R.I.C.E treatment for ankle sprains is necessary to prevent an acute injury becoming chronic, with ligaments that remain weakened and susceptible to re-injury. It is important to stop activity straight away with a sprain, and begin the ice, compression and elevation phases. Ice should be applied for 20 to 30 minutes and repeated every two hours. Severe sprains may require an x-ray for fracture assessment. Mobilisation exercises within a pain-free range of motion need to begin as soon as possible and daily. The exercises should aim to increase the range of motion and strength in the ankle, and re-train the ankle's balance receptors (proprioceptors). Ankle taping will provide further support in activity during the healing phase as can high-sided sports shoes when playing sports such as basketball and tennis, where rapid movements in different directions need to be made.

When in university I sprained both ankles badly playing soccer but did not follow the R.I.C.E procedure properly. As a consequence my ankle ligaments remained weakened and I re-sprained them a number of times before undertaking extensive physiotherapy to strengthen them. I had to wear inflatable ankle braces whenever playing sport for months afterwards; have ultrasound on the ankles; do balance exercises on a 'wobbleboard' (a round board that balances on top of a metal dome); follow a comprehensive programme of ankle stretching and strengthening exercises; and massage the ankles to break up the scar tissue already formed. My ankles have recovered well but I still get a slight sprain every now and then. I have also found that with a mild sprain, in addition to doing the R.I.C.E sequence, performing **"Bowen"** movements around the ankle straight away has resulted in a pain free ankle for me the following day. You will need to find someone who knows this technique though. In brief, a Bowen therapist moves their fingers at specific locations and in specific directions over soft tissues. The aim is to promote healing of injuries and various organic complaints and to stimulate and rebalance the body's energy systems.

Achilles tendinitis

The Achilles tendon attaches the calf muscles to the heel bone and can be easily felt just above the heel. The symptoms of this complaint are soreness around the tendon and there may also be swelling. Pain may lessen during activity, but will be worse again afterwards. The tendon can fully or partially rupture if a sudden performance that is too intense is required of the calf muscle. In this case there will be severe pain in the calf and a full rupture will need a cast and possibly surgery. Achilles tendinitis is an **overuse injury** (an injury sustained from repeated actions), but there can be a number of causes. These include over training and especially hill training; sprinting; running too often and too far too soon; changing from soft to hard surfaces; having flat feet; tight hamstring (back of thigh) and calf muscles; wearing high heels too much; and wearing running shoes that are too soft or too worn under the heel. In each case the Achilles tendon is subjected to a lot of strain with the repetitious foot pointing movements or is continually over stretched by a dropped heel.

Teenage runners can also experience heel pain where the Achilles attaches to the growth plate in the heel. A growth spurt can cause the bones to grow faster than the surrounding soft tissues, and if this occurs the Achilles can create extra strain on the growth plate.

Treatment involves reducing the inflammation and preventing the problem recurring. Icing the tendon for 15 minutes after activity will help reduce inflammation. A physiotherapist may also use ultrasound and other devices, and orthotics that raise the heel slightly or offer necessary arch support may solve the problem. Massage will help to relieve muscle tension, improve circulation and prevent scar tissue forming in minor tears. Each run should include a warm-up, cool down and stretching.

A good stretch for the Achilles is to push against a wall with one leg in front of the other. The front leg should be bent and the back leg straight, with feet pointing forwards. Push the hips forward and hold the stretch. You should feel the stretch up through the calf muscle of the back leg. Another way to stretch the area is to stand on the edge of a step or kerb so that the heels carefully drop lower than the step. These stretches should be continued even after recovery to help prevent a recurrence.

An effective recovery regime is to have a week or so of modified rest (swimming, walking etc.) then begin to run very short distances on alternate days, slowly and without hills or on very hard surfaces. Have a rest day after each run. Increase the distance gradually and continue with stretching exercises. Keeping the stride length short can also help as you gradually resume pain-free activity.

I have noticed that when you feel ongoing tightness in this area of the leg, it is no good to keep on training hoping the problem will get better. It just gets worse until you do something about the cause of it. Try stopping during a run to stretch the tight area, but if it still feels uncomfortable running it is better to stop the run and walk home than keep running into an injury.

Shin splints

This term refers to pain felt in the front of the lower leg along the shinbone (the tibia) and can involve muscle, tendon, bone or a combination of these. Due to repeated stresses during training, injury occurs when the muscle fibres tear slightly (usually the anterior and/or posterior tibialis muscles) and pull away from the bone. There may also be a stress fracture of the bone, which is a small crack line in the bone that can turn into a full fracture if not heeded (at this stage running will have to be stopped until the injury heals). Pain, swelling and warmth occur from the resultant inflammations and these are most commonly felt on the lower inner side of the tibia. Beginning runners often experience this problem as their muscles try to adapt to the new workloads. Other causes can include anything which flattens the foot, such as poor shoes, being overweight, and hard surfaces; a sudden change in training habits (run length, pace, run surface); hill running; or poor leg/foot alignment.

Another shin complaint known as **anterior compartment syndrome** affects the large shin muscle below the knee (anterior tibialis muscle) on the outer side of the tibia. As the muscle strengthens and enlarges over time with training, the size of the compartment the muscle is encased in can restrict its growth. This leads to internal pressure on the tissues and nerves and causes pain that worsens unless the problem is treated. In severe cases surgery may be necessary to relieve the compartment pressure. This was a complaint experienced by some of the people I cross-country skied with, as the skating technique required constant foot flexing repetitions to lift the ski off the snow, and this affected the anterior tibialis.

Shin splints can be prevented and treatment is similar to that for the injuries already discussed. After activity, ice the affected area for 15 to 20 minutes to reduce inflammation, and treat the cause of the problem. To prevent shin splints, do a warm-up (e.g. walking) and stretching before all training and more of the same after each session as a cool down. Shin strengthening exercises where the toes are flexed towards the head will help, as will a stretching programme for the back and legs, and good running shoes. Daily massage treatments can also be very beneficial and can be done by you at home.

Knee pain

"**Runner's knee**" is the term commonly used for pain that is felt behind, around and within the knee joint. The kneecap or patella is held in place by a tendon which attaches above to the quadriceps muscles and which goes over the kneecap to the patellar tendon below the knee. As the leg flexes at the knee, the bony patella moves by sliding up and down through a groove in the thigh bone (the femur). With repetitious movements as in long-distance running, pressure between the patella and the groove is increased and this can lead to irritation that then leads to inflammation. Pain is aggravated by running downhill, and by doing bent knee activities such as kneeling or climbing stairs.

Added irritation occurs if the patella does not track in a straight line through the groove, but travels more to one side. This is called Chondromalacia Patella, and as well as the accompanying pain and inflammation, degeneration of the patella can occur with time as the underside wears out. This can arise if the inner quadricep muscle is weaker than the outer ones so that there is an uneven pulling on the patella.

Pain on the outside of the knee can be due to tightness of the iliotibial-band, which runs from the gluteal (buttock) muscles and crosses over the outside of the knee joint to connect on the tibia. The pain may also radiate down the side of the leg from the hip. Massaging and stretching of the band can be very effective in relieving tension. Pain behind the knee can be pain referred from hamstring muscles (at the back of the thigh) that have become too tight with over-training.

The cause of knee pain can often be traced to problems such as an old knee injury, excessive pronation, having flat feet or knock knees, using old worn shoes, being overweight, or having inflexible muscles in the back of the leg (including the Achilles tendon). If unsure of your problem, begin treatment by obtaining specialist advice.

If knee pain occurs when you are running, you can try stopping to stretch and massage the affected area, slow down, eliminate downhills, avoid uneven surfaces, or if running on a slanted surface have the sore knee on the downhill side to decrease the amount of knee bend. Inflammation should be treated with ice for 20 minutes after running and this should be repeated two or three times per day. Any activity that causes pain should be avoided. Physiotherapy, orthotics and/or new shoes may be needed. Stretching of all the leg muscles should be part of each warm-up and cool-down and exercises that strengthen the quadriceps will help improve knee stability.

In Chapter 5 I mentioned how I was having a problem with inner knee pain after 45 minutes of running. The problem was fixed once I wore a thin knee strap that encircled the leg just below the knee and over the patellar tendon. The ends of this particular sort attached behind the knee with velcro pads. The idea of the strap is to guide the patella straight through the groove by keeping some pressure on the patellar tendon. It also helps to lift the patella slightly. This happened to work extremely well for me during the marathon and I still wear it whenever I do a long distance run. Such knee bands can usually be found in sports stores, but make sure the particular brand is suitable for your leg shape. A band that is too wide or has scratchy surfaces will not make running comfortable.

Muscle strains

A strain is a pull or tear in the soft tissues and is most likely to be experienced by an endurance runner in the calf or upper leg (quadriceps and hamstring) muscles. They can also occur in the associated tendons or at the muscle/tendon or tendon/bone attachments. A strain is classified by degrees. A first-degree strain involves muscle soreness that puts you out of action for a few days. A second-degree strain means you have a partial tear in the tissues and the recovery time ranges between two and four weeks. This is the type of strain I experienced in the calf muscle during training (see Chapter 5). The most severe or third-degree strain involves a rupture of the tissue and can take from one to three months to heal. By comparison, tendons and ligaments generally take longer to heal then muscles because the blood supply to them is not as plentiful as for muscles. A basic mend for broken or fractured bones takes around six weeks or more.

The signs of a muscle strain are easy to recognise. One minute you'll be running along and in the next there will be a sharp pain in the affected muscle that brings you to an abrupt halt. The muscle will also feel tight and you won't be able to put all your weight on the affected leg. There are a variety of causes of strains, and quite often it is a combination of factors at a given time that leads to one. The factors can include insufficient recovery time between sessions, a sudden increase in tempo or stride length (such as sprinting at the end of a run) or a misplaced footstep. Inadequate flexibility, cold muscles due to insufficient warm-up (especially on cold days), or an imbalance in the strength between the muscles of the front and back of the leg can also cause problems. One warning sign can be increasing tightness in a muscle over training sessions, another is that the muscle may cramp as it gets closer to tearing point.

It is important to apply the R.I.C.E sequence as soon as possible when a strain has occurred, especially as intra-muscular bleeding can be involved with serious tears. Alcohol should be avoided as it dilates blood vessels, which can increase any bleeding. R.I.C.E is followed by the appropriate physiotherapy and medical treatment whilst abstaining from running. Normal walking should recommence as soon as possible, along with gentle stretching exercises to restore flexibility. Applying massage once the acute phase is over (generally after two or three days) will promote circulation to the area, remove oedema (excess fluids), and prevent scar tissue formation. Massage should not be applied earlier to 2nd- or 3rd-degree strains.

Once the strain is responding to treatment, exercise can begin with very short, slow jogs, which gradually increase in length each day. Wait until the muscle is completely free of tightness before attempting any faster paced runs. Keeping stride length a bit shorter than usual helps to decrease the stress placed on the recovering muscle/s. Strengthening programmes are useful to ensure that strength in opposing muscles and between each leg is balanced, thereby decreasing the risk of strains due to uneven strength development. With long-distance running, the hamstrings can become stronger than the quadriceps, so extra strength training for the quads may be needed.

Cramp

This is a painful involuntary tightening of a muscle, which occurs most often in the calf but can occur in any muscle. The possible causes of cramp include – dehydration, a dietary mineral imbalance, an early mild strain, poor blood circulation to the muscle and muscle fatigue. Downhill running can also encourage cramp development.

To alleviate cramp, stretch the muscle gently – if the muscle is contracted instead of stretched the pain will intensify, e.g. if there is a cramp in the sole of the foot, bend the toes with your hand back towards your shin until the cramp stops. Massaging the affected muscle can help, and stretching a muscle that is tight before or during exercise can also prevent a cramp occurring. Other preventative steps include drinking enough hydrating liquids, remaining flexible with regular stretching, having a balanced diet to ensure proper mineral levels, and having regular massages to work tension out of and improve circulation to the muscles.

Sciatica and back pain

Lower back pain can be a common distance runner's problem as this is where the pounding forces are highly concentrated. A runner of average weight subjects his or her back to literally tons of force (moving up through the legs), even over short distances. The pressure is even greater in someone who is overweight for his or her body frame. If in addition to the jarring effects of running there is also a structural problem in the lower body (such as flat feet), then over time a condition known as **sciatica** can manifest.

Sciatica is a condition associated with the sciatic nerves. The nerves at the base of the spinal cord merge to become two large nerves called the sciatic nerves. The largest nerves in the body, they run one each side down through the back of each buttock and leg. If one or both of these nerves are irritated or pinched then the resultant pain is called sciatica. Initial pain may be experienced as a dull ache in the lower back, the middle of the buttock or in the thigh of one or both legs. The pain will intensify with continued running and can be felt radiating from deep in the buttocks to down the back of the leg and even to the ankle. There may also be a burning feeling and numbness in the leg/s. Movements such as bending the back and straight leg-raises increase the pain. Rest can remove the pain but it usually recurs again once running is resumed. In some cases sciatica may prevent a runner from walking, let alone running.

There are many causes of sciatica. Wrong lifting or twisting movements can cause a vertebral disc to slip (herniate) and then pinch the nerve. Wearing of the vertebral discs; a growth (tumour) that presses on the nerves; and physical abnormalities with the foot arches, knees or leg length – added to the jarring of running – can lead to sciatic irritation. Muscles in the back or thighs that are strengthened unevenly or are inflexible might also be implicated, as can a combination of factors related to poor training methods.

Initial treatment of sciatica includes rest, as continued running will only worsen the nerve irritation. Anti-inflammatory substances and muscle relaxants may be needed to remove the nerve inflammation and loosen any muscles that are in spasm. Massage is beneficial in relaxing tightened back and leg muscles. The cause of the sciatica will need to be determined to prevent a recurrence of the injury, and appropriate physiotherapy undertaken to rehabilitate and strengthen the affected tissues.

Backaches that are not specifically sciatica can be due to muscles that are not flexible enough. Runners with lower back problems commonly have weak abdominal muscles or very tight hamstrings with little flexibility in them or the lower back. Tight thigh muscles cause the pelvis to become less mobile, and as the shortened front of thigh muscles pull it down, a greater curve and more pressure is created in the lower back. To help minimise the chance of back pain occurring it is a good idea to regularly follow a programme of exercises that:

* strengthen the abdominal, back and hamstring muscles (e.g. abdominal curls; bent knee sit-ups with unclasped hands close by the ears; back raises, and hamstring curls)
* enhance flexibility in the quadriceps and back muscles (e.g. quadriceps stretch – standing upright, hold and take foot up behind leg towards buttock; seated toe touches; lying on the back and bringing one or both knees to the chest; and flattening the back when lying)
* reduce pressure on the spine and improve its alignment (e.g. hanging from a bar by the arms or upside down in specific hanging boots)

Knowing when to stop

Prevention of injuries is always better than having to cure them, and one of the best anti-injury principles to follow is to have enough rest days mixed in with the training days. If an injury is incurred or seems about to occur, stop the exercise and assess the situation. If there is tissue damage, follow the R.I.C.E procedure and seek a professional opinion if there is uncertainty about the extent of damage. Follow up with the appropriate treatment and rehabilitation.

Other situations during training or racing when it would be wise to consider stopping activity include: pain bad enough to make you modify your gait; sciatic pain or tingling from the buttocks to the foot; feelings of dizziness; chest pains with shortness of breath; signs of hypo or hyperthermia with weather extremes; officials who want you to stop; and any other body signal that instinctively doesn't seem right. Even if it is a last minute decision not to run because of an existing injury, there will always be more runs to participate in.

Chapter Eight Summary

⇨ Be knowledgeable about the various factors that can lead to running injuries.

⇨ Deal with minor complaints before they become more serious.

⇨ Remedy the cause of the injury rather than just treating the symptoms.

⇨ When determining cause, check for physical abnormalities, incorrect training methods, or inadequate running shoes.

⇨ Initiate the R.I.C.E sequence straight away with most injury occurrences.

⇨ Rest and proper rehabilitation are essential to speedy recovery.

⇨ Training again too soon after an injury increases the risk of re-injury.

⇨ Increase or change training factors by no more than 10% per week.

⇨ Minimise injury risk by including a warm-up and cool-down in each session, and following a regular programme of strengthening and flexibility exercises.

⇨ Injuries can be prevented by heeding early warning signals from the body.

⇨ Always consult a professional if unsure about the severity of an injury.

Chapter Nine
The Final Weeks

"Failure is a state of mind."

Tapering training

Ideally your preparation to date will have been injury-free, and once you have done the final LSD run scheduled, things really get exciting. A few weeks prior to the marathon the bulk of the training is over and will now "taper". This means that you still exercise to maintain fitness and condition, but more easily over shorter distances. This allows the body to rest, recover and enter the marathon strong and energetic. Don't liken this period to the time just before an exam when cramming information in at the last minute can help you pass. Trying to cram extra training into the last few weeks to make up for missed training sessions or feelings of doubt about making the distance is more likely to lead to depleted energy reserves or injury than a better marathon performance.

In this programme there are 3 - 4 weeks between the final LSD run (of around 3 hours) and the marathon. After that LSD run the longest run is for 1 hour, and is scheduled in the following week. The runs during the week prior to marathon week are only up to about 45 minutes in duration. During the actual marathon week there are only two scheduled runs of around 30 minutes each and a couple of short walks to keep the muscles loose. Speak to other runners who have successfully completed the marathon distance, and you will probably come up with a variety of different tapering programmes and opinions about what is the best sort of lead-up to a marathon. Keep in mind that the aim during the final week is to do a minimum of exercise in order to conserve your energy, but just enough to prevent the muscles from feeling sluggish.

Staying healthy

If all has gone to plan you will be feeling happy about how the rehearsal runs have gone and be comfortable with the different aspects of the marathon. These include the distance and your pace, what you wear, and the liquid/food you consume when running.

Having survived your unique training experiences to this stage, it is likely you will worry about getting ill in the last couple of weeks – I know I did! After having devoted so much time to training, a "self-protection" phase tends to come into play. For me this included refraining from any physical activities other than running in case I accidentally sprained an ankle in aerobics, or pulled a muscle doing gym work etc. I avoided public and smoky or crowded places as much as possible (especially hospitals) to minimise the possibility of contracting a cold or other illness, and I paid extra attention to eating healthily, getting plenty of sleep, and not getting too stressed about anything. It might sound a bit extreme, but I didn't want any physical illness preventing me from stepping up to that start line! Even then you need to be alert to dangers. A friend related an incident where just before the start of a marathon, he was stung on the leg by a wasp. The ensuing pain and swelling forced him to withdraw at the halfway mark – *c'est la vie!* (French for "that's life!")

Race information

It is usual to pick up your **race number and information** some time during the last few days before the marathon (unless the organisation posts it). Where and when to do this should be explained on an earlier confirmation of entry letter. This letter or some other pass must usually be presented before you can collect your race bag. It is handy to collect this bag as early as possible so that you can familiarise yourself with the run details. These include exactly when and where the start is, public transport details, where your start position is (there are usually groups based on previous marathon completion times), arrangements (if any) for retrieval of discarded clothing at the start, location of the drink stations, and a map and profile of the actual course. Apart from your start number, there may also be a commemorative T-shirt and some other items from the run sponsors in the bag.

If the organisation uses **"chip"** time recording you will also need to pick up a "chip", if you don't own one yourself. This is a small round plastic device that is attached to the top of one shoe so that it can record your time as you pass over electronic timing mats placed at the start, finish and at other regular intervals along the course. A chip can usually be bought or borrowed (with a deposit) from the organisation, and can also be used at other international marathons that use this recording system. If borrowed, the chip is returned straight after the race or posted back shortly afterwards, otherwise you lose the deposit (fl.45 at Rotterdam '98). One advantage of such timing is that you get the real time it took you to complete the course. If as an amateur you are positioned somewhere at the back of the field, then the start signal may occur a few minutes before you reach the start line. So your time will not actually begin until the chip registers that you have crossed the start mat. Due to the huge number of participants at the start, my official finish certificate showed there was a four and a half-minute difference between the start signal and when I even reached the start line!

I found it useful to drive around the actual course prior to the

The Frenchies will look after me!

day, just to see where I would be running and to familiarise myself with particular landmarks that I could recognise again when running past. If this is not possible, then it is reassuring to know at least what the last few kilometres of the course look like (to recognise when you are nearly finished). If you only have time to view the course the day before, then some organisers will charge an extra fee to do this. It can also be helpful to talk to others who have run that particular marathon for advice on how best to run the different sections and where any difficult parts are.

Other preparations

You might find that the nightly weather forecast on television becomes much more interesting than usual in the week leading up to the marathon! It is advantageous to have an idea of what the weather conditions will be like on the day so that you can decide ahead of time which clothes you are likely to wear. You can also start to psyche yourself up mentally if the conditions are not looking too favourable. Running in bad weather conditions is a little easier if you have done some training in similar conditions. Fortunately, for my Rotterdam experience the snow and gale-force winds occurring at the start of the week gave way to storms, then showers and finally it cleared up to be on the day, partially sunny at 13 degrees Celsius and with only a slight breeze. I have to admit that I definitely felt relieved!

Have **toenails** clipped several days before the marathon to prevent them cutting into the toes after several hours of pressure on them. Some runners are prone to ingrown toenails. This problem usually occurs due to the nail having been cut too short, being torn or being encased in shoes that are too tight. The skin at the end of the toe then sits over the end of the nail. As the nail keeps growing under the skin, pain and possibly infection can be experienced as the corner digs into the flesh. To heal, the nail must be pried from under the skin. Refraining from wearing shoes and massaging the skin away from the nail corner may solve the problem, otherwise a minor operation may be required.

Shaving under the arms can cause skin to be more sensitive to chafing, so allow some time between shaving and the run.

It is a nice advantage if you can manage to have an **assistant** with you on the day. Mart made my experience more enjoyable by being at the start to take care of my warm-up clothing, and then meeting me at different points around the course to encourage me on and take photographs as a unique record of my achievement. If you attend the marathon on your own, then ensure that you have a plan for where to leave possessions you have taken to the race but don't want to run with. This would include items like warm-up clothing. You might have to wear only what you intend to run in, as it may not be possible to leave clothing at the start with the organisation. It is not uncommon to see runners wearing a big plastic garbage bag (with holes for their arms to go through) over the upper body before the start, so that they can discard it just before beginning without having to worry about trying to find clothes after the finish.

Another.way you can prepare yourself mentally is to come up with some **motivational sayings** that can be used during the run if things start getting tough. These could relate to scenarios in which you might get a cramp, you are having trouble with the weather, or if you have "hit the wall" and are starting to doubt your ability to make the full distance. The idea is that you repeat prepared sayings to yourself in order to convince your body that it can keep going (unless you should pull out for health reasons). A few examples that worked to spur me on were – 'You're doing really well, just keep a nice even pace and enjoy what you're feeling, really savour the challenge!' and 'I have about 20 minutes left to run – that's just like going out for a really short training run – I can do that!' and 'It looks like the last few kms will have a headwind, but it's nowhere near as strong as some of the winds I trained in!' Remember all the effort you put into preparing for this day, think of the finish line getting ever closer, and know that there are many people who will never experience the thrill of what you are now achieving. During some training runs I also visualised myself really enjoying the whole marathon experience and crossing the finish line elated, which did in fact happen. The mind is very powerful, and in a marathon, state of mind can be just as important as the state of your physical self.

Chapter Nine Summary

⇨Training should taper in the lead-up to the actual marathon.

⇨Being misguided into training too much too late can do more harm than good.

⇨Take extra care to ensure remaining healthy right up to the marathon.

⇨Familiarise yourself early with the relevant race details.

⇨Don't lose your chip!

⇨Consider taking a tour around the actual course before the day.

⇨Keep an eye on the weather forecasts leading up to the run.

⇨If feasible, have a helper on the day.

⇨Prepare and rehearse some motivational sayings to help you cope better with difficult run situations that may arise.

Chapter Ten

The Big Day!

"Think and act like a winner and you'll be one!"

Finally – it's judgement day! By the end of the day you will know if all your training has paid off and whether or not you can say '! made it!' Will this turn out to be a day of elation, or disappointment? Either way, when you cross the start line you can already call yourself a winner for having had the motivation and determination needed to get there.

Final preparations

On marathon day it is best to have pre-prepared everything completely so that there is no stress in addition to that created by the inevitable "butterflies in the stomach". It is worthwhile writing out some "to do" lists ahead of time, so that you know exactly what to do and when, instead of trying to remember things at the last minute. With regard to getting your running clothes ready, doing this a few days earlier (for me it was a week earlier!) ensures that some crucial item will not be discovered too late still sitting in a pile of dirty washing!

Know and lay out exactly which **clothes** you will take and wear given any set of weather circumstances. A preparation list could look like:

- running shoes and 'chip'
- run socks and underwear
- singlet/T-shirt and shorts/leggings
- thermal underwear or other thin top, hat, gloves (for a low temperature)
- lightweight rain jacket for wet weather
- head and wrist bands
- warm-up suit (an old one if worried about not getting it back) or large plastic garbage bag
- spare set of clothes and shoes for after the race (if you have a helper or know where your clothing bag will be)

* some form of identification (best written somewhere on your race number)
* public transport ticket, and all necessary race papers including number and pass into the start area
* sunglasses and cap (if likely to be hot and you wear them)
* drink for prior to race beginning and glucose tablets (if using them)
* toilet paper/tissues in case of short supplies at the start
* for a helper to take – sunscreen, backpack, food/drink, camera, route map, spare sticky plasters, money
* Do you have a plan for what will happen to your discarded warm-up clothes?
* Have your **race number** already pinned onto the back and front of your visible running top. Make sure that it won't flap around and that it sits snugly over your stomach region. Some numbers also have space on the back for you to fill in personal details should you require medical attention. Another handy item to have and which can be taped to the underside of the number is a **phone card**.
* Have the electronic **chip** laced onto the top of one shoe. The most secure method is to actually take out the bottom part of the shoelace and then rethread it with the chip held down firmly by the shoelace going through it too – about 3 holes up from the ankle end.
* If using **public transport** to get to the start (parking places may be extremely limited on the day), know how to use it, when it operates, and have a pre-bought ticket to avoid waiting in a queue on the day. In Rotterdam, marathoners got a free travel ticket for the day and other members of the public could also get a reduced price ticket.

The night before

* Eat a meal that has worked well for you before the LSD runs (and at the same hour), don't overeat, and stay well hydrated (refer also to Chapter 6).
* Watch the local weather report for a final check on the forecast.
* Arrange for a morning wake-up call if necessary, allowing plenty of time.
* Have everything set out ready to go (including breakfast utensils

etc.), so that everything can run on automatic the following morning. Ensure you are relaxed before going to bed by reading, or listening to music etc. – you might also want to do some gentle stretching.

+ If you're religious (and maybe even if you're not!) pray for good weather, and get at least as much sleep as you would normally.

Marathon morning

I remember that the first thing I did after waking up on marathon day was to go to the window to see what the sky looked like! This allowed me to make a final calculated guess as to what the race conditions would be like so that I could dress appropriately. Keep in mind though that the start is usually several hours later than when you wake up, so the conditions could change.

+ Eat a light breakfast two to three hours before start time, consisting of what has worked well for you before the LSD runs. This is typically food like cereal, toast with honey or jam, bananas, and so on. Avoid greasy foods and large amounts of meat that will sit in your stomach too long. Drink caffeine-free liquids.

+ A lubricating gel like Vaseline can be applied to areas such as the armpits, around the toes, and inner thighs if they tended to chafe in training. I used a sticky plaster around each little toe to help prevent blisters.

+ It can be best to put on the clothes you will wear during the run before you travel to the start (as long as you have a way to stay warm). If there are changing-room facilities available, you may find crowds of people wanting to use them, and queues tend not to create a very relaxing pre-race atmosphere.

+ Pay extra attention to tying and double knotting your shoelaces, so that the shoes feel completely comfortable on your feet. I remember practically living in my running shoes during the last week until they felt like they were a part of me!

+ I found it beneficial to do some gentle stretches before leaving home to loosen up my body and help settle my mind.

+ With a large marathon the public transport system will probably be extra busy with people travelling to the start. Arriving late adds an extra stress of having to battle against floods of people to get to the start area, so allow plenty of time to get there and find your start position.

At the start

Having arrived safely at the venue, the idea is to find your start place, warm-up, then relax and enjoy the atmosphere created by so many fellow runners. The usual procedure is to position runners in groups. This is based on the completion times of their fastest recent marathon (written on the entry forms). The front group will consist of the fastest runners and then the next fastest behind them and so on, back to the slowest and first-timers at the tail end of the start area. Advantages of starting so far back are – that it's a fun atmosphere, (that's where I started!) and there is no body-crushing stampede at the start either!

The following list outlines some of the points worth remembering:

- Try not to get cold whilst waiting. Take off outer layers of clothing at the latest possible time before the start. Do some warm-up stretches and if it's really cold, huddle in amongst the other runners!

- A warm-up run is not necessary unless you plan to run fast from the start. Save all the energy you can for the actual run – the first few kms will act as the warm-up anyway.

- Long toilet queues can be a problem, so go before leaving home and once again (or more often if necessary) before the start. Being nervous before an event annoyingly makes you want to keep visiting the toilet!

- 20-30 minutes before the start, drink at least one glass of water for final hydration.

- If you have a helper, agree on a specific meeting place where you can easily find each other after the race. A recognisable feature close to the finish is good, as you don't want to have to walk too far.

Run tactics

These following tips are handy to remember to make the run progress smoothly from start to finish:

- Just before the start signal, relax yourself with some deep breaths and acknowledge that you're about to have a fantastic run.

- After the signal it may not be possible to begin running straight away, so just walk with the other participants and start your own stopwatch as you step across the start line.

♦ It is really important to settle into **your own rhythm** as soon as possible and not get tempted by other runners to run faster than you would have in training. A pace that is too fast early on can mean "hitting the wall" earlier than you might have done otherwise. It is safer instead to pick up speed in the latter stages of the race when you are confident of finishing.

♦ Be prepared to actively dodge slower runners in front for several kms after the start to avoid tripping over their heels. At times I had to run on the adjacent pavement to get around people.

♦ It can be handy to run with someone who seems to have a similar pace to yours. This helps pass the time more quickly and you can encourage each other during any tough parts.

♦ Checking the organisation clocks in the first few kilometres will help you monitor your run pace.

♦ Drink at every drink station – you might choose to walk and drink or drink on the run. Once finished with the drink cup, throw it out of the way to the side.

♦ If you want to use the wet sponges at the sponge stations, use them to dampen your face and head, but not so wet that your attire will be uncomfortable. As they may have been trampled on and reused by other runners, don't drink from them for health reasons. Sponging your legs can lead to problems like cramp later on, especially if the temperature is cool.

♦ If there is a noticeable headwind, run behind someone of a similar pace who is larger than you to help break the air stream.

♦ Wherever possible run the **inside** of a corner. Taking the outside means running more steps, and the less steps you have to run over the entire 42.195km, the happier you'll be at the end!

♦ If things start getting tough, use your prepared motivational sayings, and in the latter stages eat some glucose tablets if you have them. Even world record holder Tegla Loroupe had to fight off leg problems and fatigue in the 1999 Berlin marathon. Afterwards she remarked that she hadn't expected to set a record anymore at that point in the run, being nearly 30 seconds off her Rotterdam pace. But she toughed it out – and set another world record! (2:20.43).

♦ In the event of having to pull out of the run, find an official to inform. Hand your chip back in and then get whatever is necessary (clothing, food/drink, medical aid etc.). If this happens, keep in mind that even the best runners have "off" days. In the 1999 Rotterdam marathon I escorted an elite Brazilian female runner to the finish line when she pulled out at the halfway point. Her English was extremely limited but it was easy to know where she wanted to go when she kept repeating 'finish'? At the other end of the scale was the Dutch "hare" or pacesetter — Kamiel Maase — who intended to pull out after the 21km mark. He in fact felt so good that he ultimately ran the entire distance and finished 12th overall in 2:10.10, only 3 seconds behind the first Netherlander, Greg van Hest (2:10.07).

♦ In the last kilometre focus on looking ahead for the finish banner and keeping an even tempo. After having run so far at the same pace, a sudden attempt to sprint over the finish line can lead to an injury.

♦ As you cross the finish mats, click off your stopwatch — and smile!

Straight afterwards

Regardless of how long your marathon run took, congratulate yourself on your outstanding achievement! Stepping across the finishing line can be a very emotionally charged moment — I

"This is fantastic!" and the gloves are coming off.

know I was completely overwhelmed by the realisation of having "made it".

Have some of the drinks and food usually provided in the finish area, get some warm clothes on if it's cold, get out of the sun if it's hot, hand your chip back in, and keep moving around. Even though that may be the last thing you feel like doing, some easy walking around and stretching will help keep the blood circulating in the legs and help begin the removal of the cellular waste build-up created during the run. This has the effect of diminishing the degree of muscle soreness that will be felt in the following days.

Keep drinking in the hours after the run to begin replenishing the body's liquid stores. Warm drinks straight after the finish tend to be easier on the stomach than cold ones. Avoid eating too much too soon as the body needs a chance to get over the run exertion first.

When ready to travel home, be aware that your legs will not take kindly to having to walk down flights of stairs (or up). As I tried to slide down the handrail of the subway steps it was funny to see all the other runners also trying to get down them without bending their legs – the joys of running a marathon!

Chapter Ten Summary

⇨ Have everything prepared ahead of marathon day.

⇨ Allow plenty of time to be in the start area and feeling relaxed about the run.

⇨ Revel in the party-like atmosphere in the start area.

⇨ Establish your own running pace right from the start.

⇨ Drink small amounts regularly during the run.

⇨ Run the inside corners.

⇨ Be mentally strong.

⇨ After the finish, re-hydrate, keep warm and continue to move around.

Chapter Eleven

What to Expect Afterwards

"Being a participant in life beats just watching it go by you!"

Happy memories

The post-marathon feelings of elation at "having gone the distance" will stay with you for weeks, months and even longer after the event. They are rekindled every time somebody congratulates you or asks how it went. As you eagerly keep recounting your story to willing listeners over time, it will gradually change from an "every single detail" version to a more succinct one. Nevertheless, it is wonderful to receive all the comments about 'how amazing you are to have run so far', etc.

On marathon day evening, I sent a detailed fax back to my family in Australia, trying to give them an idea of what it felt like to take part in a marathon (see "Fax to Family"). They enjoyed the story and were even able to share some of the emotion I tried to convey to them. Also nice was getting unexpected phone calls from friends keen to know how I'd gone (even writing this brings a smile to my face again as I remember!). I made sure to put my participant's medallion in a place where I can see it every day to remind myself of what I can achieve when I set my mind to it.

The local Rotterdam newspaper prints a full list of marathon finishers and their times in the following day's edition. Find out if you can purchase something similar with your chosen marathon. It is fun to have some overall results so soon after the run to figure out how many runners were ahead (but more importantly) behind you. Otherwise you will need to wait for some official results to be sent. I received a certificate four weeks after the event – it must take a while to prepare over 10,000 of them! Information on the certificate included my full and half marathon times, my overall and age group placings, and my split times for each 5km. From this I was able to observe that – my first 5km were the fastest; each 5km section became progressively slower; my time between 10 and 20km was the most constant; the 21km time put me on schedule for a 4-hour marathon; and my final 5km were almost 7.5 minutes slower than the first 5km! Such observations come in useful when you think about whether or not your performance lived up to pre-run expectations, and how you could improve different areas for future marathon training (if you decide to do more).

The memories were relived when, after several weeks, a large photograph arrived in the mail. A professional photo service had taken shots during the whole day and then mailed them to individual runners. If you liked the photo, then you could pay for it and keep it and even order more. There was also an order form for a variety of special marathon remembrance T-shirts – I thought I should have at least one official photo and T-shirt to remember my first marathon! Still the forms kept coming – an entry form for the following year's marathon, and subscription forms to different running magazines. This marathon running could turn out to be an expensive sport!

The "after" shot, with my well-earned medallion

Recovering

My sorest muscles the day after the marathon were without a doubt the quadriceps (front thigh). It was clearly evident when I tried to walk that they believed they had done more than enough exercise for a while, as I had some difficulty co-ordinating them in a walking manner! However, the soreness diminished remarkably quickly within the next few days. Stairs are difficult to handle early on in the recovery stage, and I have heard of runners walking backwards down them to avoid the pain. My other leg muscles seemed relatively good, and didn't feel sore as much as they did heavy. Both reactions are common to long-distance runners but different runners will experience varying degrees of discomfort, based on their level of conditioning. Some athletes will begin training again a few days after the marathon, whereas others may not get back into regular training for weeks or even months. One rule of thumb is to **allow one day for every mile** (1.6km) of the marathon before beginning with hard training again. That equates to almost a month of recovering with only easy training.

For the first two weeks after the run, I did only long, easy walks, lots of stretching, and some short bike rides. Tempted in the first week to see what running would feel like, a few steps with legs that felt like they were made of lead was enough to convince me that a longer recovery period was necessary. Once I did begin running, my ankle was still recovering, so even though I was keen to start again I could only do very short runs initially. It took me four weeks before I started running for 30 minutes or more – and finally clicked my stopwatch off my marathon time and back to zero! It actually took nearly two months before I could run properly without feeling any ankle pain. Make no mistake – the marathon can really tear you down for a while!

One of the best guides to recommencing training is simply to be aware of how your body is responding to the run. A few days (weeks or whatever you need) after the marathon, begin with some runs that are slow and easy. Even then you can be misled into thinking too early that you have fully recovered from the marathon. Getting into training too quickly at this stage, when your body's defence systems are still a bit down, can easily lead to a bout of illness. If you are considering doing another marathon in the near future, allow enough time between it and the last one to properly recover and train. Aim for three or four weeks of recovery, 12 or so weeks of training and two to three weeks to taper.

Another stage of recovery is the **psychological** part of wondering what to do next, once the marathon is over. That 42.195km was the big goal, so what will motivate you to keep training now? I had said that one marathon would be enough for me, then I would go back to shorter training runs just to keep in good physical condition. The memory of how tough a marathon is (the first time anyway) does not fade rapidly, and I was quite happy to have successfully completed a marathon. I was not looking ahead to another one. However, by the day of the 1999 Rotterdam marathon, the memories of any discomfort and pain had definitely dimmed, and as I was taking photographs of the competitors I was experiencing some feelings of regret at not also being one of the running crowd again!

Chapter Eleven Summary

⇨ Expect to feel quite a degree of soreness in the leg muscles. This should diminish within the next few days, but full recovery will take much longer.

⇨ Help remove the soreness by doing some stretching, having warm baths, taking some relaxed walks, and having a gentle sports massage.

⇨ Allow plenty of recovery time before resuming training.

⇨ Begin running again with short distances and a slow pace.

⇨ Listen to your body to know if you are doing too much too soon.

Chapter Twelve
Stretching Exercises

"Stay in touch with your inner self to keep in balance."

The photographs in this chapter show the exercises I do in my warm-up and cool-down routines. I tend to spend twice as long doing the exercises in the cool-down to ensure well-stretched tissues after the training session. As you can see from the photographs, no special room or equipment is needed to perform these stretches.

Important tips to remember when stretching are:

* Work gradually into a stretch position to the point of muscle tension, but never pain.

* Stretch to within your limits. If you can't stretch as far as shown in the photos, just take the stretch as far as is comfortable for you.

* Don't bounce or jerk the muscles during a stretch as this can overstrain the tissues.

* Hold the position still and for a duration of 10 to 30 seconds/counts.

* Repeat the stretch several times, relaxing between each repeat.

* The muscles and soft tissues may not be very warm before a training session (especially an early morning one) so take extra care with pre-training stretches.

* Incorrect stretch technique or stretching too soon after an injury has occurred can delay healing.

* Ensure that all muscle groups to be used during training are stretched.

* Stretch regularly to help improve flexibility and prevent tension-related injuries.

* Shake arms and legs loosely to end the stretching session.

These photographs show the stretch performed on one side of the body only. Stretch on one side then swap positions to repeat the stretch on the other side.

Calf stretch – keep back leg straight and with feet flat on the ground. Toes of both feet point forwards.

Back of legs – straighten the front leg after the first stretch so both legs are as straight as possible. Lean over the front leg to best feel the stretch.

Back stretch – push outside of elbow against the opposite outside knee and turn the torso in the direction away from that elbow. Place other hand on lower back (don't be alarmed if you hear 'clicking' sounds as the spine loosens). This can also be done in a sitting position.

Front thigh stretch – stand straight and lift leg gradually up behind the body until resistance is felt.

Advanced inner thigh stretch – slowly lift the leg up from the prior stretch and extend it backwards. Try to keep upper body upright.

Back of legs and back stretch – keep legs as straight as possible, lower head towards knee and reach hands towards the ankles. Do sitting down if prone to back aches.

Extra flexibility stretch – keep legs as straight as possible, with hands reaching down as far as possible.

Groin stretch – have front leg bent. This can also be done in a lunging position with the other foot on the ground.

Back of legs – keep legs as straight as possible. This can also be done in a seated position with legs straight.

Upper back stretch – a good one for between the shoulder blades, the hands are clasped together. This can also be done in an upright position with hands clasped and lifted up behind the back.

Knee rotations – bend legs and rotate the knees in one direction for several circles. Repeat in the other direction. This is also a good warm-up exercise for skiing!

Ankle rotations – circle the ankle in one direction several times before repeating to the other side.

The above stretch descriptions are only a selection – there are many other effective stretches. Others that I like to do include **pelvic rotations** (hands on hips, legs apart and straight then move the hips in a circle several times in one direction, then in the other) and **side-lunges** (legs apart and straight, then bend one knee out to the side and hold, keeping the knee over the foot). When sitting on the floor in front of the television, some good flexibility exercises to do include – putting the soles of the feet together and pressing the legs down towards the floor; having legs stretched out in front then lowering the chest and head towards the legs; and also giving the knee joints and feet a good massage.

Chapter 13
Fax to Family – 20/4/98

Dear everyone – <u>I MADE IT!!</u>

Thanks for your "good luck" wishes – I'm sure they helped along with all the other ones I received from other people. I finished the entire <u>42.195km in 4 hours, 12 minutes and 4 seconds</u>. It was such an amazing day that I want to share it as much as possible with all of you – the entire world even!

At the start of the week the weather was so dreadful – snow, endless downpours of rain, hail, gale-force winds, you name it – we had it. Every day I watched the weather reports trying to gauge what Sunday's weather would be like, and prepare myself psychologically. On Sunday the 12th Mart drove me around the entire course, so I could see where I would be running – it seemed like a very long way even in the car! That was a nice idea though, because on race day I could recognise the various landmarks we had passed in the car.

On March 16th I did a training run of 2hrs 45m according to the programme. The last 20 mins were hard – my right calf muscle cramped, I had sore ankles, my right thigh was tight and my left knee had begun to ache after only 45 mins. After 1.25hrs I had to stop every 6 minutes and massage it to be able to run another 6 minutes. I also had sore tendons on the tops of my feet and my little toes blistered. I couldn't see how I would possibly be able to run for at least another hour in the marathon. I was feeling a little discouraged at this stage.

One week later (4 weeks before the marathon), I ran a shorter distance of 1hr 25 mins. The shorter distance was nice but I still had the same problems with ankles and knee. The final long run of 3 hrs was scheduled in one week's time. I decided not to do it, feeling that my injuries would only worsen and not be recovered in time for the marathon. From then on I did 3 or 4 runs each week of 30-45 minutes. On April 3 I knew I was registered to run when I saw Fl.75 had been withdrawn from my account for the entry fee.

On Monday of marathon week it snowed. That night I had a gentle massage from a friend to make my muscles feel as good as possible. I did two short, easy runs on Tuesday and Thursday and made sure I did some yoga every day. Still it rained and galed. For the last 2 weeks beforehand I was pretty strict with my diet – low fat (very difficult over Easter!) and lots of fruit and veggies. I had my race clothes picked out ready the weekend before the event, for good and bad weather conditions. Anxiously watching the weather reports it looked as though there might be a break in the weather.

Friday night we drove into town to pick up my number from the "Ahoy" sports and entertainment building – Janet Jackson was giving a concert that night. We had to park about 10 mins from the building because of other competitors having already filled the car park. There was a sports exposition on at the same time, and we stopped at one stand to look at an elbow brace for Mart's "tennis" elbow (too much plastering work). At the same time I looked at a knee band that was supposed to help with knee pain while you played sport. Quite a narrow band, it just straps across the bottom of the patellar tendon and fastens with velcro at the back of the knee. But should I risk getting it and wearing it in the marathon? Mart bought his armband and when I finally decided to buy the knee band, Mart discovered he didn't have enough money in his wallet to pay for it and I had forgotten to take mine. I wondered whether it might have helped, as my knee was my main concern for being able to complete the run. After I had shown my race licence, I was given my number – F224, then a T-shirt and other bits and pieces in the show bag. Then Mart was rummaging around in his wallet and counting small change, saying that there was probably enough change to add to the notes if I wanted to go back and buy the knee band. So I did. I wore it for the rest of the night, and for a few hours the next day, and I wondered how comfortable it would feel when I was running, and whether it would do more harm than good. At least I could take it off easily if it wasn't helping.

Saturday, and finally the weather had improved a bit. I took a leisurely walk, did my yoga exercises and made sure that everything was ready for the Big Day. We visited friends that afternoon, and sat outside in the sun until it clouded over again. It seemed like an early test of willpower not to have any of the chips that were in bowls on the table. Friends and strangers alike wished me luck for the following day, and I told them I was probably going to need it. My aims for the run? 1 – to finish, 2 – if No. 1 happened, then aim for 4 hours. That night we ate chicken breasts with veggies, salad and rice. I did some more stretching, had everything prepared for the next morning, and we were both in bed by 10.30 p.m.

Race Day: I was up at 8am looking out the window at the sky – cloudy, would probably be a bit windy, but no sign of rain so far. I started fixing breakfast and making food for during the day. Mart was going to be my run assistant, so I packed a parcel of sandwiches, fruit, muesli bar, sultana buns and a packet of yoghurt sweets for him – it was all eaten too! At 8.45 am I had 2 kiwi fruit (no skins today!), tea, water, and two pieces of toast with 2 bananas. Then I carefully dressed into what I thought would be right for the day – comfortable undies, bike shorts and a very well worn but light 12-year-old T-shirt, maybe a bit cold to start with but ok if it got to the predicted 13 degrees. Then my special running socks, sweat band and wrist wallet with 8 energy tablets inside. The day before I had spent time pinning my numbers onto the shirt and attaching the round electronic timing device to my right shoe with the laces holding it firmly on. It would record my running time every 5km when I passed over special mats on the road. I pulled my hair tightly into a ponytail then sprayed hairspray all over it so that the wind would not blow it about. I put a hair band on my hairline as well. Then I put my shoes on, the knee band and finally a tracksuit over everything to stay warm. Mart took a photo' of me trying to look tough.

Mart was going to ride his bike around parts of the course to encourage me along, so he carried a backpack as well. In that I had a wet weather running jacket, a ski hat, X-C ski racing gloves, sunglasses, long tights in case the weather turned too cold for shorts, a baseball cap, our food, a camera and drinks. It was 10.30am.

One last quick visit to the toilet then we headed for the metro station 200m away. Mart would come home after the start then take his bike in the car to an easy to park place, and ride from there. There were already a lot of people on the metro but we both got a seat in the end. The man sitting opposite was running for the fourth time. He recalled his first marathon and said how nervous he had been. Mart noticed from the sudden tears in my eyes that I must have been a touch nervous too! About 25 minutes later we stepped out with the masses and went up the steps to the street above, very close to the start area. 11.00am, and some of the 10,250 participants had already started to line up. Lots of portable toilets luckily, so another final nervous pee and then I felt ready. Being a first-timer I had to line up right in the back section, so we stood waiting with our backs to a street pole, to avoid being pushed from behind. I spoke with a woman close by – this was her 7th marathon. I was wondering if there were any other first-timers. I did finally find one – and we wished each other luck. For about 100m behind the start line on both sides of the street the runners began to fill all the spaces until it was almost claustrophobic. Mart kept a good hold on me and wouldn't let me take off my tracksuit too early in case I got cold. With 10 minutes to go I took it off anyway, and a group of French runners let Mart know that they would take good care of me during the run! One of them also grabbed my camera and got Mart to take a photo of us all.

Every now and then the whole crowd would surge forward a little as everyone tried to move ahead. Five minutes to go and suddenly there were clothes being thrown over to the sides from all directions by runners getting down to the bare minimum. I noticed a lot of runners in long tights and long sleeves, or wind jackets. It was quite cool, so I decided to wear the gloves that I always train with in winter and hoped that the sun would come out at some stage. Down to one minute – and a last hug and kiss from Mart. The cannon sounded, and I saw later on the television just how fast the top athletes sprinted away from the start. All of us at the back began a slow walk to the start line. Halfway to the line a guy decided that he'd better go off to the row of portable loos in the median strip, and it was almost like he'd started a stampede of men that decided they'd better get one last quick one in too! That was a good laugh.

It's about 4 minutes later when we reach the start, so it's time to click the stopwatch and take those first steps. My body feels relaxed and ready to go. I remember the advice about not going too fast at the start, so I settle into my own rhythm quickly and enjoy the cheering spectators and surrounding music. The wonderful atmosphere must be largely due to the 800,000 spectators around the course that have come out to cheer us all on.

Only about 5 minutes into the run and the sun has come out! – people in anything other than short clothes are rapidly beginning to overheat. My choice of clothing couldn't have been better! There is a lot of dodging going on as people settle into their strides and I am continually weaving in and out to better positions, even going up onto the sidewalk at times. With so many runners it can be difficult making sure the pace is not too fast. There are markers on the road for the first five kilometres – it looks like I'm taking 5.5 minutes per kilometre – maybe a little slower than what I'd have liked, but there's a long way to go. I hear a yell, and looking up I see Mart on an over-pass at about 2.5km – it's easy to wave and smile at this stage. I settle in be-hind the "7th time" woman, we seem to have a similar pace. The sensation of running with so many people after just training on my own is incredible – I can't see the surroundings for the people around me. I feel good, passing and being passed.

"Which country are you from?" I hear as a short man runs up beside me. "Do I look that foreign?" I reply. "You just look – different." I take it as a compli-ment. Bernard has come from Africa for this race and he has guessed that I'm not Dutch. We run together at the same pace for quite a way, and he tells me the history of how the Dutch first went to Africa. He is also going to do the London marathon this year and a really big run back in Africa as well. "Aren't you hot with those gloves on?" he asks. "A bit, but I'll get rid of them soon," I say. It's about 12km and I suddenly see Mart on the bike. He sees me at the same time and as he takes a photo I rip off my gloves and throw them for him to catch. "That was well done," Bernard comments. Already 1hr into the run but my right ankle is getting sore. My knee feels fine.

I look at my watch – 1hr 20 gone, it has passed so quickly. "Look again at 2 hrs," Bernard says. I see Mart quite a few times between the 12 and 20km marks. "My ankle is hurting a bit." "Just relax," he says. Bernard is ahead now, having picked up his pace. I still run at the same pace. Another drink station at 20km – I take a few mouthfuls of water. I have been having a sports drink, but have been feeling a slight stitch every now and then. I will stick with water drinks in case it is the electrolytes causing a stitch. The road ahead of me is well and truly littered with plastic cups from runners faster than I. A little past each drink station I run over a sea of yellow sponges that runners cool themselves down with. I take one for the 2nd time at 20km and put a bit of water on my head. The temperature at the mo-ment is perfect for running. I see plenty of T-shirts lining the road though that have been abandoned by overheated runners. Another common sight during the entire run is people (mostly men) relieving themselves near the bushes.

Running up a gradual incline, there is Mart in the middle of the tram tracks. "That's a good picture," he says. The tram official scoots him off the track. I hear a loud counting – 1,2,3,4,5 – and just off to the side I see the police pushing on the chest of a 55-year-old male runner who has probably had a heart attack, trying in vain to bring him back to life. His day didn't turn out the way he'd hoped, and maybe the police have the job of finding relatives in the sea of onlookers. I put it to the back of my mind for now. The halfway point – it has taken me 1hr 59m – perfect timing for a 4-hr run if I do the same time for the 2nd half. I still have to do all of that again. I kid myself and say that the hardest half is over. I've already won the battle just by getting this far in the run. I grab a sponge at the next station to wet my head a bit. Having done a loop to the south of the city we are now heading back towards but 1km from the start before heading out on a loop to the north. The crowds are getting bigger again as we get closer to the centre. A policeman at the side catches my eye and smiling, he starts to clap. I say in Dutch to him, "Thanks a lot." Then throw my very wet sponge up and at him so that he has to catch it. With a surprised look he does, and the onlookers have a good laugh with us.

The clapping and best wishes aimed directly at me almost make me start crying – it's quite an experience. It makes my throat tighten up so that I almost become asthmatic and have to open my mouth wide to gulp in air! A rock band provides lively music for a short time, it's a pity they can't be around the whole course. A long stretch coming up now between 25 and 30km, and at 2hrs 10m I see the first woman running parallel to me, but in the direction of the finish line. The tiny Kenyan Tegla Loroupe, who won last year, will go on to win the women's division in a new world record time of 2:20.47, breaking the 1985 record, about 13 minutes behind the fastest man, and taking home $200,000 American for her efforts. Wow!

This stretch along the Maas river is scenic, but the going is starting to get tough, and the skies are clouding over more. I see more people beginning to walk at around the 30km mark. Now is the time to start getting mentally tough. There is a loop of about 7.5km around a large lake. Everyone is spread out much more now, but there are always runners around me. I haven't seen Mart for quite a while and I'm looking for some extra encouragement. It seems like a long loop, but finally at 34km I see Mart again. I stop at the drink station for a bit longer than usual to exchange a few words with him. He had to ride a fair way around to be able to get onto the course again with me. He tells me of the winning times and takes some more photos. He can tell by looking at me that it is getting harder to smile. I push on again.

The "7th time" woman suddenly pulls up beside me sweating copiously. "You look good," she says, but she's the one that has the experience to be able to pick up the pace for the last 7kms. I'm happy for her, but for me it's now a case of just hanging in there. Finally the lake loop is finished and Mart has gone again. Another couple of kms of a slight incline and the temperature has dropped a bit now. It also looks like we'll have a headwind for the last part. People all around me are walking, or throwing up on the side, and yet still others are picking up their pace for the last part. I think I must have about 6km left to go when suddenly I see the 4km line across the road. That spurs me on psychologically but my body has ideas of its own. I see an unexpected final .drink station and my body almost jumps for joy at the chance to legitimately stop again for a brief respite. I stop and my right thigh goes into a little cramping spasm. I pull it up behind my back for a quick stretch to stop the cramp. I have had no muscular problems at all until now, apart from blisters on my taped little toes, but they're not too bad. My knee is fine and I pushed the ankle pain out of my consciousness a long way back.

I take a drink and keep walking – for 2 minutes. I figure I have about 20 minutes more running ahead of me. I can do that. I put both of the last 2 energy tablets into my mouth and literally hear my body groan as I take more running steps. This is tough now, but I remind myself to savour all the feelings, seeing that I have only planned on doing a marathon once. I know that I'm going to make it now, and I just keep the wheels rolling. I don't see the people on the sides so much anymore, I'm focussed on the road ahead. Still going into a headwind and the onlookers are saying, "Just a little bit further now," which is what they've been saying for the last 10km. People keep passing me, but I am still passing as well. I'm happy that I can make myself keep going.

I round the corner into the street we ran up at the start, and then there is 1km to go. It is a very slight downhill, which I am happy about. I feel a twinge in my left thigh as if my body is saying it's had enough and I make myself keep going at exactly the same pace. There is no excess energy in me for a final sprint to the line.

The force of the cheering crowd is overwhelming again and I look ahead for the Finish banner. Finally I see it and focus on the last minute of running. Now I know for sure I'll get there – and I can hardly believe I've made it. I run over the last mats, knowing that there is nothing left for any more steps. My hands are over my face as a few tears of relief and happiness spill over. The first official congratulates me and gives me a beautiful rose, the next puts a medallion around my neck. Then a plastic sheet is put around my shoulders to keep me warm and I wobble over to the food stand. Grabbing drinks, and banana and orange pieces I make my legs keep moving so that they don't seize up.

I take off the electronic timing device and hand it in to an official. I go towards the place I was to meet Mart, but only runners are allowed in that area. I wonder where he is. Still the runners stream in behind me. I start to walk out of the compound to look for Mart amongst the masses, but after 10 minutes decide I will have to find a telephone to call his mobile. He taped a phone card to the underside of my number this morning before we left home. I decide to look once more from behind the steel fence, then I see him and climb the fence to try to attract his attention. He still doesn't see me, so to the surprise of the onlookers I jump down and into the compound again, walking in his direction and hoping he doesn't move. He sees me, and a nice official opens part of the fence just so I can get to Mart. I give the official a kiss, then collapse onto Mart. Now he takes the "after" photo. I grab my tracksuit, put it on then make a dive for some cordial and a sandwich. I really needed that!

And that was how one of my most challenging goals was achieved!

Mart was really wonderful riding around after me all day. I think he rode almost as far as I ran, and he was just as tired that night! I took the metro home again, having quite some difficulty getting down the stairs to the platform. But so did the other runners following me down! I got a seat on the metro, sat back then, reflecting on my achievement, opened a well-deserved packet of Easter eggs!

When I got home I had a long, hot shower then gave my legs a massage. I couldn't believe that after running nearly 1.5hrs longer than I ever have before, my knee hadn't troubled me at all. I put it down to wearing the knee band purchased so close to race day. That risk paid off big time! In bed that night I had to lie with my legs straight, otherwise my knee ligaments would hurt. I had a slight headache too so I took a couple of Panadol and within 5 minutes the pain was all gone.

Monday – boy, am I glad I didn't schedule doing any massages until Wednesday! I'm having a bit of difficulty walking today. My quadricep muscles don't seem to want to relax, and I need to walk sort of straight legged. Sometimes a leg will decide to collapse a bit when I'm standing still, but I still say it's all worth it. I was so happy with how I went, nothing could have been any better. After a slow walk into town this afternoon to get a newspaper, I have the official results and a certificate will be sent to me shortly as well. Officially there were about 10,250 beginners, and 8,126 of them finished. My place was **6,491st** – so that means there were a lot ahead of me, but also 3,759 runners behind me! My time was 4:12, and the results showed that 4 other people crossed at exactly the same time. The slowest time was 5:12. What a wonderful day. Now I just need a few weeks of recovery time...

Lots of love to you all,

Heather xxxx

Chapter 14
Afterword

And then – in April 1999 I decided to do the famous Berlin marathon, to be held on 26 September. I sent the entry form off in June. Training was going great – until eight weeks before the marathon. After a 3-hour LSD run in France I had a pain in my left outer knee, for which I later took cortisone tablets (and which took three months to heal). Three weeks later all training came to an abrupt halt when my left thigh (just above the knee) slammed into the ground from a much harder than usual landing after a hang-gliding flight. With no ice in sight (where is an Aussie pub/bar when you need one?) and not reaching camp again until late at night, my poor thigh did not get the R.I.C.E treatment it required.

An ultrasound test on my greatly enlarged lower quadriceps muscle four weeks before Berlin revealed a reasonably solid 3.7cm thick mass of congealed blood. "Eight weeks to heal," the doctor said cheerily! Frustrated and disappointed, I turned to my marathon book for words of solace. And in Chapter 5 (Complications Along the Way), right at the end of the section titled Frame of Mind I read ....

If you would like to share your marathon experience – successes, disappointments, challenges etc., send me a letter at one of the following addresses. (Who knows? The stories might be printed into another book!)

Heather Mull, c/o PO Box 94, Mt. Beauty, VICTORIA 3699, AUSTRALIA. (Fax: +61 357 544594).

Chapter 15
Suggested Reading

Henderson, Joe. *Marathon Training - The Proven 100 Day Program for Success* Illinois (U.S.A): Human Kinetics, 1997.

Cash, Mel and Ylinen, Dr. Yari. *Sports Massage* London (U.K): Random House Ltd, 1988.

Jensen, Karen and Winterdyk, John. *The Complete Athlete* British Columbia (Canada): Alive Books, 1998.

Sleamaker, Rob. *Serious Training for Serious Athletes* Illinois (U.S.A): Human Kinetics Publishers Inc.

Your Marathon Training Diary

Two blank training diary pages are provided for you to copy freely. The author has kindly waived copyright for this purpose. They are presented on facing pages to minimise copying charges.

WEEK   BEFORE MARATHON: Date:_____

Day   **Target:** _____
Morning HR: _____ beats/minute

Run Route: _____
_____
_____

Distance/Time taken:_____

Date of last similar length run:_____

Training sort: LSD_____MD_____ Race/SFD_____Easy_____
                    Rest day_____ Other(describe)_____

Warm-up: stretches_____ **Cool down:** stretches _____
                 walk _____   walk _____
                 jog _____   jog _____

Environment:

Time:_____ **Temperature:**_____ **Wind strength:**_____ **Rain?:**_____

Food/drink before training:_____

Time (between meal & training):_____

Session description:
Positive aspects:

Problems/how to improve:

Overall Rating:

fantastic   good   OK   not so good

<u>WEEK   BEFORE MARATHON:</u>   Date:_____

Day   Target: _____
Morning HR: _____ beats/minute

Run Route: _____
_____
_____

Distance/Time taken:_____

Date of last similar length run:_____

Training sort: LSD_____MD_____ Race/SFD_____Easy_____
               Rest day_____ Other(describe)___._____

Warm-up: stretches_____   **Cool down:**   stretches _____
                 walk _____   walk _____
                 jog _____   jog _____

Environment:

Time:_____ **Temperature:**_____ **Wind strength:**_____ **Rain?:**_____

Food/drink before training:_____ _____

Time (between meal & training):_____

Session description:
Positive aspects:

Problems/how to improve:

Overall Rating:

fantastic   good   OK   not so good

Index

A

accessories 38
achilles tendinitis 94
achilles tendon 97
alcohol 37, 66, 99
altitude 33
amenorrhoea 78
amino acids 58
anaemia 60, 79
ankles 50, 93, 118, 123
anorexia nervosa 85
anterior compartment syndrome 96
Arnica 51
aromatherapy 51

B

back 121-123
back pain 100, 101
basic run 12, 17
Beams, Adrienne 74
blisters 40, 48, 111
Body Mass Index 87
Bowen 94
Bras 82
breakfast 65, 71, 111
breathing 44
   rhythm 31
bulimia 85

C

caffeine 28, 62, 66
calcaneus 92
calcium 79
calf 50, 51, 98, 121
calf muscle 46
carbohydrate 28, 54
Castro, Domingos 3

C

cellulite 56, 64
certificate 116
chafing 36, 83, 106
chip 105, 110, 113
CHO 65-66, 71-72
chocolate 70
cholesterol 56
Chondromalacia Patella 97
clothing 26, 36-37, 39, 41, 107, 109
compression 91
contraceptive pill 76, 82
cool-down 27, 64, 120
cosmetics 83
cramp 29-30, 82, 99-100, 113
cross-training 25

D

dehydration 28-30, 61-62, 85, 99
diary page 19, 21-22
diet 63, 66
dinner 68
distance 1-2, 12
drink 27-28, 44, 64, 72, 113

E

eating disorders 84
elevation 91
entry fee 6

F

fatigue 28-29, 79, 86
fats 54-58, 67-69, 73
feet 92
fibre 54, 60, 71
flexibility 51, 91, 122, 124
food combining 67
foods 27, 44, 71, 77

foot tendon 48
free radicals 59

G
glucose 55, 72
glycogen 55, 65, 72
groin 122

H
hamstring 98
handicaps 3
headaches 29, 51, 75, 77, 82
heart rate 32, 80
heat exhaustion 29
heat stroke 29
heel spurs 92
hills 31
"hitting the wall" 30, 55
hormones 75, 76, 81
hypothermia 37

I
ice 91
illnesses 33
inflammation 48
ingrown toenails 106
injuries 27, 45, 47, 51, 52, 80,
    90-91, 93, 95, 97, 99, 101, 120
intervals 10, 13
iron 60, 79

K
kilocalories 56
knee 39, 45, 49-50, 123
knee pain 96
knee strap 98
Kosgei, Japhet 4
Kristiansen, Ingrid   3

L
laces 48
lactic acid 27
laxatives 86

leg pain 42
legs 121-123
ligaments 90, 98
Loroupe, Tegla 3, 4, 113
losing weight 64
lower leg 95
LSD runs 13, 16-18, 26, 28, 48, 50,
    62, 64, 71, 103, 110
lunch 66

M
Maase, Kamiel 114
make-up 83
marathon day 14, 71, 109, 111
marathon rehearsals 25
margarine 67
massage 47, 50, 52, 88, 91, 95, 99,
    101
MD run 13, 16-17
megadosing 59
menopause 78, 81
menstruation 60, 75, 78-79
minerals 54, 59, 77
motivation 107
muscle strains 98
muscle tear 46
muscle tenderness 50

N
nicotine 66
night before 110

O
oestrogen 76, 78
Olympic Games 2, 74
orthotics 39, 93, 95
osteoporosis 78
over-training 11, 34, 97

P
pace 12, 14, 16-17, 113
pain 90

pelvis 124
periodisation 11
plantar fasciitis 92
PMS 76
post-marathon 116
pregnancy 78, 80, 81
pre-menstrual syndrome 75
preparation list 109
progesterone 76
pronation 92, 97
protein 54, 58, 66

Q

quadriceps 50, 98, 101, 117

R

R.I.C.E. 91, 99, 102
race information 104
race number 104, 110
recovery 117-119
   time 47, 50
rest days 14, 15, 18, 43, 102
Rotterdam 3, 3, 5, 10, 16, 30, 72,
   105, 110, 116

S

salt 66
scar tissue 47, 91
sciatica 100, 101
SFD 12-13, 17, 27
shin muscles 50, 51
shin splints 95, 96
shivering 37
shoelaces 34, 111
shoes 38, 41, 49
snacks 68
soreness 119
sponges 113
sports drinks 29, 62
sprains 91, 93
starches 54
start 104, 112

stitch 30, 44-45
strain 90
strength workouts 9
stress 87
stretching 27, 120-121, 123
sugars 54
supplements 60
Switzer, Katherine 74

T

tapering 103, 119
tendons 90, 98
time limit 5
time of day 24
timing 105
tingling 102
toenails 106
training 3, 88, 103, 108, 118
   diary 18, 133
   programme 10, 14
   time 4
   tips 34
   travel 43

U

ultra-marathons 1
upper leg 98

V

van Hest, Greg 114
vegetarianism 58
vertebral disc 100
vitamins 54-55, 59, 79

W

warm-up 27, 120
water 54, 61
weather conditions 4, 25, 106
world record 3, 113

Y

yoga 44, 77, 88

 **– your first choice for outdoor leisure books.**

As one of the leading UK leisure book publishers, we have a wide range of books covering:

⊙ **UK & European Walks**

⊙ **Mountain Biking**

⊙ **Football**

⊙ **Angling**

⊙ **Golf**

Contact us for a free catalogue or visit our web site at:

www.sigmapress.co.uk

SIGMA LEISURE, 1 SOUTH OAK LANE, WILMSLOW,
CHESHIRE SK9 6AR.
Phone: 01625-531035 Fax: 01625-536800.
E-mail: info@sigmapress.co.uk

MASTERCARD and VISA orders welcome.